# Test Practice
# Grade Three
# Table of Contents

M000115585

# Skills Tested on Standardized Tests
## for Grade 3

| | CAT/5 (Level 13) | CTBS (Book A) | ITBS (Level 9) | MAT/7 (Elem 1) | SAT (9th ed) (Primary 3) | TerraNova (Level 13) | TAAS (Level A) |
|---|---|---|---|---|---|---|---|
| **Word Analysis** | | | | | | * | |
| Recognizing Beginning Sounds | X | X | | | | | |
| Recognizing Ending Sounds | X | X | | | | | |
| Recognizing Vowel Sounds | X | X | | | | | |
| Forming Compound Words | X | X | | | | | |
| Finding Prefixes | X | | | | | | |
| Finding Suffixes | X | X | | | | | |
| Finding Root Words | X | X | | | | | |
| **Vocabulary** | | | | | | * | |
| Identifying Synonyms | X | X | X | X | X | | X |
| Identifying Antonyms | X | X | | X | | | |
| Understanding Word Meaning | X | X | X | | X | | |
| Recognizing Words in Context | X | X | | | X | | |
| Analyzing Affixes and Roots | X | X | | | | | |
| Understanding Multiple Meanings | X | X | | X | X | | |
| **Reading Comprehension** | | | | | | | |
| Identifying Passage Details | X | X | X | X | X | | |
| Determining Sequence of Events | X | | | X | X | X | X |
| Understanding Word Meaning from Context | X | X | | X | X | X | |
| Understanding Cause and Effect | X | X | X | X | X | X | X |
| Understanding Character Traits | | X | | | | X | |
| Identifying Main Idea | X | X | X | X | | X | X |
| Identifying Supporting Details | | | X | | | X | X |
| Predicting Outcomes | X | X | | X | X | X | X |
| Distinguishing Between Fact and Opinion | X | | | X | | X | X |
| Recognizing Genre | X | | | X | | X | X |
| Identifying Author's Purpose | X | | X | X | X | X | |
| Drawing Conclusions | X | | X | X | X | X | X |
| **Spelling, Language Expression, and Language Mechanics** | | | | | | | |
| Identifying Correct Spelling | X | X | X | X | | | |
| Using Capitalization and Punctuation | X | X | X | X | X | X | X |
| Identifying Misspelled Words | | | X | X | X | | X |
| Determining Correct Usage | X | X | X | X | X | X | X |
| Identifying Subject and Predicate | X | X | | | | | X |
| Combining Sentences | X | | | X | X | X | |
| Identifying Topic Sentences | X | | | X | X | X | |
| Identifying Supporting Sentences | X | X | | X | X | X | |
| Analyzing Paragraphs | X | X | X | | | | |

* TerraNova integrates these skills into Reading Comprehension.

Test Practice 3, SV 3787-9

# Skills Tested on Standardized Tests
# for Grade 3

| | CAT/5 (Level 13) | CTBS (Book A) | ITBS (Level 9) | MAT/7 (Elem 1) | SAT (9th ed) (Primary 3) | TerraNova (Level 13) | TAAS (Level A) |
|---|---|---|---|---|---|---|---|
| **Mathematics Computation** | | | | | | | |
| Using Computation | x | x | x | x | x | x | x |
| (Adding, Subtracting, Multiplying, Dividing) | x | x | x | x | x | x | x |
| **Mathematics Concepts/Applications** | | | | | | | |
| Understanding Numeration | x | x | x | x | x | x | x |
| Understanding Counting | x | x | | x | | x | x |
| Understanding Place Value | x | x | | | x | x | x |
| Understanding Whole Numbers, Fractions, and Decimals | x | | | | x | | x |
| Using Probability | | | | x | x | x | x |
| Working with Graphs, Charts, and Tables | | x | x | | x | x | x |
| Understanding Measurement and Geometry | x | x | x | x | x | x | x |
| Working with Number Sentences | x | | x | x | | x | x |
| Using Estimation | x | | x | x | | x | x |
| Understanding Number Theory | x | | | | | x | |
| Understanding Patterns and Relationships | x | | | x | x | x | |
| Using Problem-Solving Strategies | x | x | | x | x | x | x |
| Solving Word Problems | x | x | x | x | x | x | x |
| **Study Skills** | | | | | | | |
| Understanding Book Parts | | | x | x | x | | |
| Using the Dictionary | | | x | x | x | | |
| Using Reference Materials | | | x | x | x | | |
| Analyzing Visual Information | | | x | x | | | |
| Using the Library | | | x | | | | |

Standardized achievement testing is a fact of life in public and private schools. As the United States continues moving toward applying national standards for achievement at each grade level, standardized testing will take on even greater importance to the public. Expectations for education are changing throughout the country as performance standards for students in all grades are being raised. The high-tech world of the twenty-first century will require that students acquire more sophisticated reading, writing, and math skills. Evaluation of how well the schools are helping our students meet the new national standards is the primary focus of many standardized achievement test programs.

With so much emphasis on the goal of achieving high test scores, it's not surprising that some teachers and administrators feel apprehensive when test schedules are announced. In turn, this sense of apprehension is often transmitted to their students. How can we make standardized test-taking a positive educational experience for students? Teachers and parents can familiarize themselves with the format of, the skills covered by, and the test language used in the standardized tests used in their schools. Teachers and administrators are often asked, "What's on the test?" While specific answers to that question are not available, teachers and parents should be knowledgeable about what skills students are expected to know as they progress through school. Teachers and parents can give students the tools to assist them in improving test-taking skills. Students can be taught how to read and listen to directions, how to use an answer sheet, how to budget their time during a timed test, and even how to control test stress.

### Standardized Achievement Tests

While there are many standardized tests available, the following tests are administered in grades 2–6, cover the test areas of vocabulary, reading comprehension, spelling, language, mathematics, and study skills, and were selected as the basis of this test practice series. The CAT/5 is the *California Achievement Tests, Fifth Edition*. The CTBS is the

*Comprehensive Tests of Basic Skills*. The ITBS is the *Iowa Tests of Basic Skills*. The MAT/7 is the the *Metropolitan Achievement Tests, Seventh Edition*. The SAT is the *Stanford Achievement Test, Ninth Edition*. The TAAS is the *Texas Assessment of Academic Skills*. The *TerraNova* is the new replacement for the CTBS and is the most recent achievement test to reach the school market.

### Interpreting and Reporting Test Results

The standardized tests that elementary students frequently take, as noted on the Skills/Achievement Tests Grid on pages 2–3, are norm-referenced tests. These tests are administered in uniform testing conditions, and they compare the performance of the student to a representative sample of students from the nation's public schools. The test results are generally provided in percentile form. For example, suppose a student scores in the 68th percentile. This indicates that this student performs better than 67% of all the students in the national sample—and not as well as 32% of the students in the sample. In many school districts, parents receive standardized test results for their children either at parent conferences or through written communication. School districts often report test results by individual school for local publication in newspapers. States sometimes compare the scores of individual school districts. Standardized tests provide one measure of students' academic progress. Standardized test results are most effective when also used in conjunction with classroom assessments, which are more diagnostic in nature.

### ORGANIZATION

This book contains nine units, and each unit focuses on a specific test-taking skill area: Word Analysis, Vocabulary, Reading Comprehension, Spelling, Language Mechanics, Language Expression, Mathematics Computation, Mathematics Concepts/Applications, and Study Skills. These nine skill areas were selected by comparing the components of the commonly used standardized tests listed in the Skills/Achievement Tests Grid on pages 2 and 3. You can use this Skills/Achievement

# Test Practice
# Grade Three
# Introduction

Tests Grid to review which skills students are generally expected to know by the end of the third grade. This will enable you to plan practice lessons emphasizing those skills. Check the Skills/Acievement Tests Grid for the standardized tests that your school will be using.

The main test areas included in this series are described below. For more definitions of testing terms, refer to the list of definitions on page 7.

- **Word Analysis**
  This test measures students' recognition of beginning and ending sounds, recognition of vowel sounds, recognition of sight words, ability to form and recognize compound words, and recognition of prefixes, suffixes, and roots.

- **Vocabulary**
  This test measures students' knowledge of synonyms and antonyms. The emphasis now is on measuring a student's ability to make use of the context containing multiple meanings of words.

- **Reading Comprehension**
  This test measures a student's basic understanding of the meaning of an informational passage, a narrative selection, or a poem. Going beyond the literal comprehension level, the emphasis is on measuring a student's ability to interpret, analyze, and evaluate text.

- **Spelling, Language Mechanics, and Language Expression**
  These tests emphasize the writing process. The Spelling test focuses on the ability to identify correct spelling. The Language Mechanics test focuses on the ability to handle the editing process, including identifying correct spelling, using capitalization and punctuation conventions, demonstrating knowledge of subject and predicate, and demonstrating correct usage. The Language Expression test measures sentence and paragraph development, use of topic sentences and supporting details, ability to combine sentences, and understanding of writing conventions.

- **Mathematics Computation**
  This test measures the fundamental operations of basic math instruction by testing a student's

ability to demonstrate proficiency in the computation procedures of addition, subtraction, multiplication, and division.

- **Mathematics Concepts/Applications**
  This test measures the ability to demonstrate an understanding of numbers and number relationships and to apply concepts to visual representations of problems. This test also evaluates a student's ability to apply problem-solving strategies to identify information, use patterns and relationships, apply estimation strategies, and solve computation problems.

- **Study Skills**
  This test measures a student's demonstrated proficiency in using various reference materials and information-processing skills.

**Multiple Forms**

This book includes four forms of each test because some students need more practice than do others. You might decide to use one form as a pretest and another form as a posttest. Or, you might photocopy one form of a test and use it for both a pretest and a posttest, while using the other forms as daily practice sessions in between administering pre- and posttests. Or, you might choose to use the forms as homework assignments, sending one test home at a time.

**Record Forms**

- The Individual Record Form on page 8 can help you summarize each student's strengths and weaknesses in the specific skills of a test and help you decide what skills a student should practice further.
- Completing the Class Record Form on page 9 will give you an overview of skill areas for planning appropriate instructional activities for small groups or an entire class.
- The Answer Sheet on pages 123–124 is a separate bubble-in form. We have provided a generic answer sheet in addition to allowing students to indicate their answer choices on the actual test pages. You may choose to photocopy the answer sheet for each student to use with each test, or you may choose to have them write answers on test

pages. Because there are four forms of each test, you may choose to alternate the way in which your students answer the test questions.

## USE

The *Test Practice* series is designed for independent use by students who have had prior instruction in the specific skills covered in the tests. These tests are intended as practice to get students feeling more comfortable with the test-taking environment and procedures. Copies of the tests can be given to individuals, to pairs of students, to small groups, or to an entire class. They can also be used as homework or as a center activity.

To begin, decide the implementation that fits your students' needs and your classroom structure. The following plan suggests one format for implementation:

1. Review the tips below.
2. Send the Letter to Parents on page 10 home with students so family members can help.
3. Review the Skills/Acievement Tests Grid on pages 2–3 to know the skills included. Then check the Table of Contents to locate which test you'd like to administer. Photocopy those pages. Decide if students will use the Answer Sheet on pages 123–124 or write their answers on the test pages.
4. Explain the purpose of the practice test to your students. Review with students the procedures for how you want them to conduct themselves during the test; see the tips below.
5. Do a sample item together and discuss it.
6. Use a timer to time the students during the test; monitor them also. Assure them that these pages are for practice purposes only and they are to do their best.
7. Use the Answer Key on pages 125–128 to check students' answers. Then record the scores on the record forms on pages 8–9.

## Getting Started: Tips for Teachers

Here are some helpful ideas for teachers to do before administering a standardized test. Discuss test-taking strategies in general with students with emphasis on these points:

- The test is timed; practice using the time efficiently. Practice using a timer to begin and end activities of 10–20 minutes.
- Practice ways to avoid making errors, such as looking closely at item numbers and corresponding answer sheet numbers or completely erasing a wrong answer.
- Be sure that students understand the directions for each test before they begin to work independently. Complete sample items together and discuss the thought process for selecting each answer. Discuss how to apply logical reasoning to choose the best answer choice.
- Discuss when and how to guess.
- Decide how many days per week you will practice test-taking skills and plan for it.
- Set aside a sufficient block of time for each test you plan to administer. Use the time limits printed at the end of each test as your guide.
- Make your room environment as close to a real test situation as possible.
- Ask students to sit in separate desks and spread out.
- Remind them not to talk during the test.
- Put a "Testing—Do Not Disturb" sign on the door.

## Tips for Students

Here are some tips to discuss and practice with your students before they take a standardized test.
- Stay calm. Focus on the task.
- Look over the entire test section before beginning.
- Read all the answer choices before choosing one.
- Have some scratch paper on hand for math problems.
- Complete all the test questions, but don't spend too much time on any one item.
- Do not ask questions during the test.
- Check to be sure the test question numbers match the answer sheet numbers.
- Take all the time allowed; reread the questions and your answers if you finish early.

Here are some terms to know concerning standardized achievement testing.

**achievement test**  A test that measures student knowledge resulting from specific instruction.

**age equivalent**  The score derived from age norms on a standardized test established by determining the average score made by students of each age.

**age norms**  The typical or average performance on standardized tests for students in different age groups.

**criterion-referenced test**  The measurement of proficiency in specific curriculum areas by evaluating a student's degree of success in completing prescribed tasks; it tells what a student is able to do.

**deviation**  The difference between one set of values/scores and the mean.

**diagnostic test**  A test used to discover the nature and, if possible, the causes of inability to perform average scholastic tasks.

**frequency distribution**  A table for classifying test scores according to the number of times they occur in a group evaluation.

**grade equivalent**  The score derived from grade norms on a standardized test.

**grade norm**  The mean raw score obtained by students in a particular grade.

**intelligence test**  A series of tests that measure general mental ability or scholastic aptitude.

**mean**  The point on a scale above and below which the deviations are equal.

**median**  The point on a scale below which half of the scores in a frequency distribution fall.

**norm-referenced test**  A test based on standards determined by testing a large number of students of different age or grade placement; it tells how a student compares with others.

**percentile rank**  The position assigned to a score when the scores are divided into one hundred equal divisions in descending order.

**portfolio assessment**  This method of tracking a student's progress involves selecting chronological samples of a student's work that can be compared to show the progress over time and storing the samples in a folder.

**reliability**  The consistency in test results; the degree to which a test's results actually measure what a student can do on a given test.

**rubric**  A scoring guide based on a scale for rating a group of students' papers.

**standardized test**  A test for which norms on a reference group are provided; a test with specific procedures such that comparable measurements may be made by testers in different geographic areas.

**stanine**  One of nine standard divisions of test scores with the fifth stanine representing the average or mean score and a standard deviation of two.

**validity**  The degree to which a test measures what it is designed to measure or that it can predict performance on other measures.

Name _____ Date _____ Form _____

## Individual Record Form

| | Number Correct | Retest? |
|---|---|---|
| **Word Analysis** | | |
| Consonant Sounds/Beginning and Ending | | |
| Vowel Sounds | | |
| Compound Words | | |
| Root Words | | |
| Contractions | | |
| Sight Words | | |
| Prefixes and Suffixes | | |
| | | |
| **Vocabulary** | | |
| Synonyms, Antonyms, Homonyms | | |
| Word Meaning | | |
| Words in Context | | |
| Multiple Meanings | | |
| | | |
| **Reading Comprehension** | | |
| Main Idea, Supporting Details | | |
| Author's Purpose, Genre, Predicting Outcomes | | |
| Cause and Effect, Conclusions, Sequence | | |
| Fact and Opinion, Character Traits | | |
| | | |
| **Spelling, Language Mechanics and Language Expression** | | |
| Spelling, Capitalization, Punctuation | | |
| Usage, Subject, Predicate | | |
| Sentence Combining, Paragraph Analysis | | |
| Topic Sentences, Supporting Statements | | |
| | | |
| **Mathematics Computation** | | |
| Basic Computation | | |
| | | |
| **Mathematics Concepts/Applications** | | |
| Numeration | | |
| Probability | | |
| Number Theory | | |
| Fractions, Money, Measurement, Geometry | | |
| Number Sentences | | |
| Mathematics Relationships | | |
| Graphs, Charts, Tables | | |
| | | |
| **Study Skills** | | |
| Dictionary | | |
| Reference Materials | | |
| Library, Book Parts | | |
| Visual Information | | |

# Class Record Form
## Form _____

| Students | Word Analysis | Vocabulary | Reading Comprehension | Spelling | Language Mechanics | Language Expression | Mathematics Computation | Mathematics Concepts/Applications | Study Skills |
|---|---|---|---|---|---|---|---|---|---|
| | | | | | | | | | |
| | | | | | | | | | |
| | | | | | | | | | |
| | | | | | | | | | |
| | | | | | | | | | |
| | | | | | | | | | |
| | | | | | | | | | |
| | | | | | | | | | |
| | | | | | | | | | |
| | | | | | | | | | |
| | | | | | | | | | |
| | | | | | | | | | |
| | | | | | | | | | |
| | | | | | | | | | |
| | | | | | | | | | |
| | | | | | | | | | |
| | | | | | | | | | |
| | | | | | | | | | |
| | | | | | | | | | |
| | | | | | | | | | |
| | | | | | | | | | |
| | | | | | | | | | |
| | | | | | | | | | |
| | | | | | | | | | |
| | | | | | | | | | |
| | | | | | | | | | |
| | | | | | | | | | |
| | | | | | | | | | |

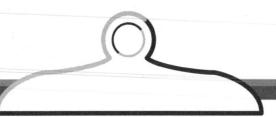

**Dear Parent,**

At some time during this school year, our class will be taking standardized tests. Because we want children to be familiar with the format and language of the tests they will likely be taking, from time to time we will practice with sample tests. Test-taking can be a stressful experience for many children. By giving them the tools to help them feel comfortable, we can reduce their stress level.

Please consider the following suggestions for helping your child perform as well as he or she is able on the test:

- See that your child gets a good night's sleep, especially on the night before a test.
- Make sure he or she eats a healthy breakfast.
- Review any content areas that your child might feel uncertain about.
- Practice with your child the use of a timer to start and end an activity.
- Remind your child about general test-taking strategies, such as:
  - stay calm and focus on the task
  - listen to or read all the directions
  - look over the entire test or section before beginning
  - read all the answer choices before choosing one
  - don't spend too much time on any one item
  - take all the time allowed; look back over your answers.

If your child expresses anxiety about taking the tests, talk about what might be causing these feelings. Then talk about ways to overcome these feelings. Above all, assure your child that the practice tests provide an opportunity for him or her to improve skills that will help when the actual tests are given. Having your support plus the knowledge of good test-taking skills will go a long way toward improving your child's standardized test scores.

Thank you for your help!

**Cordially,**

# Test 1 (Form A) Word Analysis

**Following are directions for teachers/parents to say to administer the student test on the next pages. Take time to make sure students mark the correct answer in each sample. Answer the students' questions before starting each test. Allow a total of 20 minutes of time, not including time on samples, for students to complete the test items.**

**SAY:** On this page you will match consonant sounds with the beginning and ending sounds of words. Look at Sample A. Darken the circle next to the word that starts with the same sound as *then*.

Allow students time to find and mark their answers.

**SAY:** You should have darkened the circle for letter **C**, *there* because *there* begins with the same sound as *then*.

Be sure that students understand what they are expected to do.

**SAY:** Now you will find more words that <u>begin</u> or <u>end</u> with the same sounds. Put your finger on number 1. We will do numbers 1 through 7 the same way we did Sample A. Listen as I read each question. Then darken the circle next to the correct answer.

1. Darken the circle for the word that <u>begins</u> with the same sound as *slide...slide.*
2. Darken the circle for the word that <u>begins</u> with the same sound as *drive...drive.*
3. Darken the circle for the word that <u>begins</u> with the same sound as *strap...strap.*
4. Now listen for the ending sounds. Darken the circle for the word that <u>ends</u> with the same sound as *lost...lost.*
5. Darken the circle for the word that <u>ends</u> with the same sound as *fish...fish.*
6. Darken the circle for the word that <u>ends</u> with the same sound as *tent...tent.*
7. Darken the circle for the word that <u>ends</u> with the same sound as *touch...touch.*

**SAY:** For questions 8–14 read the directions and do Sample B. Then darken the circle for the correct answer to each problem. For questions 15–20 read the directions and do the samples. Then work the problems.

**(Recommended Time: 20 minutes)**

# Test 1: Word Analysis (Form A)

**Sample A**
Ⓐ thin
Ⓑ twin
Ⓒ there
Ⓓ slap

1. Ⓐ drive
   Ⓑ sled
   Ⓒ play
   Ⓓ line

2. Ⓐ drop
   Ⓑ tray
   Ⓒ free
   Ⓓ bride

3. Ⓐ train
   Ⓑ brown
   Ⓒ stream
   Ⓓ throw

4. Ⓐ band
   Ⓑ bunch
   Ⓒ trust
   Ⓓ sting

5. Ⓐ wish
   Ⓑ wild
   Ⓒ dark
   Ⓓ wall

6. Ⓐ milk
   Ⓑ turn
   Ⓒ burn
   Ⓓ went

7. Ⓐ bush
   Ⓑ bench
   Ⓒ fern
   Ⓓ camp

**GO ON ⇨**

# Test 1: Word Analysis (Form A), page 2

**Directions:** For questions 8–14 look at the underlined vowel or vowels in the first word. Then darken the circle for the word that has the same sound as the underlined vowel.

**Sample B**

shirt
- Ⓐ tire
- Ⓑ fir
- Ⓒ mine
- Ⓓ hid

**8.** bone
- Ⓐ loose
- Ⓑ cost
- Ⓒ told
- Ⓓ bore

**9.** pen
- Ⓐ peel
- Ⓑ bell
- Ⓒ eat
- Ⓓ seed

**10.** bug
- Ⓐ tube
- Ⓑ curb
- Ⓒ butter
- Ⓓ use

**11.** toy
- Ⓐ boil
- Ⓑ court
- Ⓒ love
- Ⓓ goose

**12.** game
- Ⓐ laugh
- Ⓑ pal
- Ⓒ lawn
- Ⓓ cane

**13.** town
- Ⓐ row
- Ⓑ count
- Ⓒ rough
- Ⓓ sore

**14.** fall
- Ⓐ sail
- Ⓑ shall
- Ⓒ heal
- Ⓓ bawl

**GO ON ⇨**

# Test 1: Word Analysis (Form A), page 3

**Directions:** For questions 15–17 read each word carefully. Then darken the circle for the word that has the root word underlined.

**Sample C**
- Ⓐ <u>walk</u>ing
- Ⓑ <u>winter</u>
- Ⓒ cl<u>oset</u>
- Ⓓ <u>each</u>

15.
- Ⓐ <u>smile</u>d
- Ⓑ <u>laugh</u>ed
- Ⓒ al<u>one</u>
- Ⓓ <u>burn</u>ing

16.
- Ⓐ <u>need</u>y
- Ⓑ sur<u>prise</u>
- Ⓒ w<u>orking</u>
- Ⓓ <u>sad</u>ness

17.
- Ⓐ <u>rid</u>ing
- Ⓑ <u>fast</u>er
- Ⓒ re<u>write</u>
- Ⓓ d<u>istance</u>

**Directions:** For questions 18–20 read each word carefully. Then darken the circle for the word that shows the suffix underlined.

**Sample D**
- Ⓐ young<u>est</u>
- Ⓑ wal<u>ked</u>
- Ⓒ su<u>nny</u>
- Ⓓ tea<u>ches</u>

18.
- Ⓐ tal<u>ler</u>
- Ⓑ cold<u>est</u>
- Ⓒ foo<u>lish</u>
- Ⓓ sa<u>ved</u>

19.
- Ⓐ rai<u>ny</u>
- Ⓑ bo<u>oks</u>
- Ⓒ bark<u>ed</u>
- Ⓓ short<u>ly</u>

20.
- Ⓐ mend<u>ing</u>
- Ⓑ care<u>less</u>
- Ⓒ high<u>ly</u>
- Ⓓ spe<u>aker</u>

**STOP**

# Test 1 (Form B) Word Analysis

**Following are directions for teachers/parents to say to administer the student test on the next pages. Take time to make sure students mark the correct answer in each sample. Answer the students' questions before starting each test. Allow a total of 20 minutes of time, not including time on samples, for students to complete the test items.**

**SAY:** On this page you will match consonant sounds with the beginning and ending sounds of words. Look at Sample A. Darken the circle next to the word that starts with the same sound as *clap...clap.*

Allow students time to find and mark their answers.

**SAY:** You should have darkened the circle for the letter **D**, *clear* because *clear* begins with the same sound as *clap.*

Be sure that students understand what they are expected to do.

**SAY:** Now you will find more words that begin or end with the same sounds. Put your finger on number 1. We will do numbers 1 through 7 the same way we did Sample A. Listen as I read each question. Then darken the circle next to the correct answer.

1. Darken the circle for the word that begins with the same sound as *train...train.*
2. Darken the circle for the word that begins with the same sound as *flag...flag.*
3. Darken the circle for the word that begins with the same sound as *screen...screen.*
4. Darken the circle for the word that begins with the same sound as *thrill...thrill.*
5. Now listen for the ending sound. Darken the circle for the word that ends with the same sound as *bang...bang.*
6. Darken the circle for the word that ends with the same sound as *talk...talk.*
7. Darken the circle for the word that ends with the same sound as *hurt...hurt.*

**SAY:** For questions 8–14 read the directions and do Sample B. Then darken the circle for the correct answer to each problem. For questions 15–20 read the directions and do the samples. Then work the problems.

**(Recommended Time: 20 minutes)**

# Test 1: Word Analysis (Form B)

**Sample A**
- (A) floor
- (B) place
- (C) drum
- (D) clear

1.
- (A) true
- (B) threw
- (C) chap
- (D) when

2.
- (A) clean
- (B) state
- (C) blouse
- (D) flew

3.
- (A) green
- (B) scramble
- (C) shiver
- (D) crowd

4.
- (A) rain
- (B) drill
- (C) tray
- (D) throw

5.
- (A) wing
- (B) rink
- (C) wind
- (D) want

6.
- (A) will
- (B) tall
- (C) silk
- (D) round

7.
- (A) turn
- (B) car
- (C) dirt
- (D) hand

**GO ON ⇨**

# Test 1: Word Analysis (Form B), page 2

**Directions:** For questions 8–14 look at the underlined vowel or vowels in the first word. Then darken the circle for the word that has the same sound as the underlined vowel.

**Sample B**

d<u>i</u>ve

- Ⓐ pig
- Ⓑ window
- Ⓒ little
- Ⓓ write

8. b<u>u</u>mp
   - Ⓐ fuse
   - Ⓑ hunch
   - Ⓒ rude
   - Ⓓ ruler

9. c<u>a</u>p
   - Ⓐ cape
   - Ⓑ ladder
   - Ⓒ barn
   - Ⓓ crawl

10. n<u>oi</u>se
    - Ⓐ cough
    - Ⓑ road
    - Ⓒ boy
    - Ⓓ lost

11. gr<u>a</u>de
    - Ⓐ wrap
    - Ⓑ cart
    - Ⓒ rain
    - Ⓓ ago

12. h<u>ea</u>vy
    - Ⓐ red
    - Ⓑ weed
    - Ⓒ hear
    - Ⓓ where

13. m<u>oo</u>n
    - Ⓐ month
    - Ⓑ count
    - Ⓒ smooth
    - Ⓓ rough

14. tr<u>i</u>p
    - Ⓐ tribe
    - Ⓑ finger
    - Ⓒ file
    - Ⓓ child

**GO ON ⇨**

# Test 1: Word Analysis (Form B), page 3

**Directions:** For questions 15–17 read the contraction. Then darken the circle for the words that tell what the contraction means.

**Sample C**

I'll
- Ⓐ I did
- Ⓑ I will
- Ⓒ I would
- Ⓓ I should

**Directions:** For questions 18–20 find which word is the compound word. Then darken the circle for the correct answer.

**Sample D**
- Ⓐ colorful
- Ⓑ outside
- Ⓒ under
- Ⓓ example

15. she's
- Ⓐ she was
- Ⓑ she did
- Ⓒ she could
- Ⓓ she is

16. we've
- Ⓐ we have
- Ⓑ we will
- Ⓒ we did
- Ⓓ we can

17. couldn't
- Ⓐ could have
- Ⓑ can not
- Ⓒ could not
- Ⓓ could it

18. Ⓐ possible
- Ⓑ kindness
- Ⓒ breakfast
- Ⓓ counting

19. Ⓐ running
- Ⓑ mailbox
- Ⓒ tomorrow
- Ⓓ useful

20. Ⓐ baseball
- Ⓑ over
- Ⓒ remember
- Ⓓ spelling

**STOP**

# Test 1 (Form C) Word Analysis

Following are directions for teachers/parents to say to administer the student test on the next pages. Take time to make sure students mark the correct answer in each sample. Answer the students' questions before starting each test. Allow a total of 20 minutes of time, not including time on samples, for students to complete the test items.

SAY: In this test you will find words that you hear. I will say a word. Then you will darken the circle for the word I say.

SAY: Look at Sample A. Darken the circle for the word *mouse...mouse.*

Allow students time to mark their answers.

SAY: You should have darkened the circle for the letter C, *mouse...m-o-u-s-e.*

SAY: Now you will do numbers 1 through 7 the same way as you did Sample A. Listen as I say each word. Then darken the circle for the correct answer.

1. Darken the circle for the word *laugh...laugh.*
2. Darken the circle for the word *yellow...yellow.*
3. Darken the circle for the word *friend...friend.*
4. Darken the circle for the word *school...school.*
5. Darken the circle for the word *move...move.*
6. Darken the circle for the word *would...would.*
7. Darken the circle for the word *shout...shout.*

SAY: For questions 8–14 first read the directions and do Sample B. Then darken the circle for the correct answer to each problem. For questions 15–20 read the directions and do the samples. Then work the problems.

**(Recommended Time: 20 minutes)**

# Test 1: Word Analysis (Form C)

**Sample A**
- (A) save
- (B) happy
- (C) mouse
- (D) sleep

1.
- (A) grand
- (B) four
- (C) laugh
- (D) tooth

2.
- (A) yard
- (B) yellow
- (C) boat
- (D) you

3.
- (A) friend
- (B) from
- (C) full
- (D) first

4.
- (A) star
- (B) soon
- (C) some
- (D) school

5.
- (A) most
- (B) move
- (C) more
- (D) maybe

6.
- (A) you
- (B) want
- (C) would
- (D) were

7.
- (A) she
- (B) shout
- (C) about
- (D) shore

**GO ON ⇨**

# Test 1: Word Analysis (Form C), page 2

**Directions:** For questions 8–14 look at the underlined vowel or vowels in the first word. Then darken the circle for the word that has the same sound as the underlined vowel.

**Sample B**

st<u>a</u>ck

- (A) claw
- (B) cart
- (C) crab
- (D) strange

8. <u>a</u>bout
   - (A) after
   - (B) able
   - (C) around
   - (D) animal

9. c<u>or</u>n
   - (A) worm
   - (B) work
   - (C) form
   - (D) room

10. d<u>ay</u>
    - (A) break
    - (B) bark
    - (C) read
    - (D) seal

11. h<u>i</u>ke
    - (A) bill
    - (B) cried
    - (C) field
    - (D) bird

12. d<u>ow</u>n
    - (A) look
    - (B) blow
    - (C) soar
    - (D) loud

13. s<u>au</u>ce
    - (A) shawl
    - (B) nature
    - (C) spray
    - (D) round

14. t<u>oa</u>st
    - (A) town
    - (B) sock
    - (C) coin
    - (D) bolt

**GO ON ⇨**

# Test 1: Word Analysis (Form C), page 3

---

**Directions:** For questions 15–17 look at each underlined word. Then darken the circle for the word that can be added to it to make a compound word.

**Sample C**

sun
- Ⓐ place
- Ⓑ shine
- Ⓒ way
- Ⓓ right

---

**Directions:** For questions 18–20 read the contraction. Then darken the circle for the words that tell what the contraction means.

**Sample D**

can't
- Ⓐ could not
- Ⓑ can too
- Ⓒ can not
- Ⓓ could have

---

**15.** home
- Ⓐ store
- Ⓑ walk
- Ⓒ star
- Ⓓ work

**16.** under
- Ⓐ stand
- Ⓑ ball
- Ⓒ over
- Ⓓ slow

**17.** out
- Ⓐ in
- Ⓑ doors
- Ⓒ seem
- Ⓓ above

**18.** aren't
- Ⓐ am not
- Ⓑ are not
- Ⓒ any one
- Ⓓ and now

**19.** won't
- Ⓐ will not
- Ⓑ won it
- Ⓒ would not
- Ⓓ will have

**20.** she'll
- Ⓐ she did
- Ⓑ she will
- Ⓒ she should
- Ⓓ she fell

# Test 1 (Form D) Word Analysis

**Following are directions for teachers/parents to say to administer the student test on the next pages. Take time to make sure students mark the correct answer in each sample. Answer the students' questions before starting each test. Allow a total of 20 minutes of time, not including time on samples, for students to complete the test items.**

**SAY:** On this page you will match consonant sounds with the beginning and ending sounds of words. Look at Sample A. Darken the circle next to the word that starts with the same sound as *sleep...sleep.*

Allow students time to find and mark their answers.

**SAY:** You should have darkened the circle for the letter **D**, *slow* because *slow* begins with the same sound as *sleep.*

Be sure that students understand what they are expected to do.

**SAY:** Now you will find more words that <u>begin</u> or <u>end</u> with the same sounds. Put your finger on number 1. We will do numbers 1 through 7 the same way we did Sample A. Listen as I read each question. Then darken the circle next to each correct answer.

1. Darken the circle for the word that <u>begins</u> with the same sound as *sway...sway.*
2. Darken the circle for the word that <u>begins</u> with the same sound as *cruel....cruel.*
3. Darken the circle for the word that <u>begins</u> with the same sound as *scrape...scrape.*
4. Darken the circle for the word that <u>begins</u> with the same sound as *chop...chop.*
5. Now listen for the ending sound. Darken the circle for the word that <u>ends</u> with the same sound as *hard...hard.*
6. Darken the circle for the word that <u>ends</u> with the same sound as *match...match.*
7. Darken the circle for the word that <u>ends</u> with the same sound as *sting...sting.*

**SAY:** For questions 8–14 read the directions and do Sample B. Then darken the circle for the correct answer to each problem. For questions 15–19 read the directions and do the samples. Then work the problems.

**(Recommended Time: 20 minutes)**

# Test 1: Word Analysis (Form D)

**Sample A**
(A) lead
(B) clip
(C) chap
(D) slow

1. (A) gray
   (B) swell
   (C) tree
   (D) frame

2. (A) freeze
   (B) cry
   (C) frail
   (D) trap

3. (A) brown
   (B) share
   (C) tree
   (D) scream

4. (A) chair
   (B) ship
   (C) show
   (D) three

5. (A) warn
   (B) storm
   (C) cord
   (D) girl

6. (A) when
   (B) witch
   (C) teeth
   (D) truth

7. (A) wrong
   (B) pint
   (C) bend
   (D) went

**GO ON ⇨**

# Test 1: Word Analysis (Form D), page 2

**Directions:** For questions 8–14 choose the word that *does not* have the same sound as the underlined part of the first word. Then darken the circle for the correct answer.

**Sample B**

fi<u>sh</u>

Ⓐ wash
Ⓑ rich
Ⓒ cash
Ⓓ push

8. <u>k</u>ing
   Ⓐ castle
   Ⓑ know
   Ⓒ keep
   Ⓓ care

9. si<u>x</u>
   Ⓐ kicks
   Ⓑ exam
   Ⓒ wax
   Ⓓ socks

10. wh<u>i</u>le
    Ⓐ where
    Ⓑ who
    Ⓒ whether
    Ⓓ when

11. brea<u>the</u>
    Ⓐ the
    Ⓑ watch
    Ⓒ with
    Ⓓ this

12. <u>j</u>elly
    Ⓐ jam
    Ⓑ germ
    Ⓒ gas
    Ⓓ join

13. la<u>mp</u>
    Ⓐ limb
    Ⓑ camp
    Ⓒ limp
    Ⓓ romp

14. ma<u>sk</u>
    Ⓐ school
    Ⓑ skip
    Ⓒ science
    Ⓓ skate

**GO ON** ⇨

Name _____ Date _____

# Test 1: Word Analysis (Form D), page 3

**Directions:** For questions 15–17 read the underlined word. Look for the root word. Then darken the circle for the correct answer.

**Sample C**

<u>friendly</u>
- (A) end
- (B) frie
- (C) friend
- (D) endly

**15.** <u>bicycle</u>
- (A) icy
- (B) cycle
- (C) bicy
- (D) cle

**16.** <u>confine</u>
- (A) fine
- (B) on
- (C) in
- (D) fin

**17.** <u>national</u>
- (A) tion
- (B) nat
- (C) nation
- (D) onal

**Directions:** For questions 18–19 read the underlined word. Look for the prefix or the suffix. Then darken the circle for the correct answer.

**Sample D**

Find the prefix of the underlined word.

<u>review</u>
- (A) rev
- (B) view
- (C) re
- (D) revi

**18.** Find the suffix of the underlined word.

<u>wonderful</u>
- (A) ful
- (B) wonder
- (C) won
- (D) der

**19.** Find the prefix of the underlined word.

<u>delight</u>
- (A) light
- (B) deli
- (C) ight
- (D) de

**STOP**

# Test 2: Vocabulary (Form A)

**Directions:** For questions 1–7 look for the word that means the *same* or *almost the same* as the underlined word. Then darken the circle for the correct answer.

**Sample A**

<u>huge</u>

Ⓐ large
Ⓑ tree
Ⓒ strong
Ⓓ building

**Time: 25 minutes**

1. <u>injure</u>
   Ⓐ just
   Ⓑ journey
   Ⓒ hurt
   Ⓓ help

2. <u>above</u>
   Ⓐ road
   Ⓑ walk
   Ⓒ threw
   Ⓓ over

3. <u>healthy</u>
   Ⓐ long
   Ⓑ wealthy
   Ⓒ well
   Ⓓ short

4. <u>tap</u>
   Ⓐ chair
   Ⓑ table
   Ⓒ taste
   Ⓓ touch

5. <u>silence</u>
   Ⓐ noise
   Ⓑ quiet
   Ⓒ happy
   Ⓓ sad

6. <u>tale</u>
   Ⓐ story
   Ⓑ tablet
   Ⓒ stove
   Ⓓ teacher

7. <u>student</u>
   Ⓐ book
   Ⓑ write
   Ⓒ pupil
   Ⓓ pen

**GO ON ⇨**

# Test 2: Vocabulary (Form A), page 2

**Directions:** For questions 8–14 look for the word that means the *opposite* of the underlined word. Then darken the circle for the correct answer.

**Sample B**

strong

Ⓐ small
Ⓑ many
Ⓒ weak
Ⓓ much

8. tall
   Ⓐ full
   Ⓑ short
   Ⓒ wide
   Ⓓ round

9. after
   Ⓐ sooner
   Ⓑ later
   Ⓒ before
   Ⓓ earlier

10. quick
    Ⓐ still
    Ⓑ slow
    Ⓒ cross
    Ⓓ wise

11. polite
    Ⓐ sloppy
    Ⓑ happy
    Ⓒ rude
    Ⓓ firm

12. deep
    Ⓐ well
    Ⓑ wide
    Ⓒ broad
    Ⓓ shallow

13. borrow
    Ⓐ money
    Ⓑ lend
    Ⓒ spend
    Ⓓ buy

14. healthy
    Ⓐ happy
    Ⓑ sick
    Ⓒ sing
    Ⓓ exercise

**GO ON ⇨**

# Test 2: Vocabulary (Form A), page 3

**Directions:** For questions 15–19 find the word that would fit in both sentences. Then darken the circle for the correct answer.

**Sample C**

I wrote a _____ to my sister.
I can read a music _____.
(A) letter
(B) page
(C) note
(D) flute

15. Put the _____ back on the shelf.
I live six _____ away from my friend.
(A) toys
(B) blocks
(C) miles
(D) books

16. You need a _____ to leave the room.
Did you _____ the spelling test?
(A) key
(B) pass
(C) see
(D) read

17. Do you know the _____ answer?
Turn _____ at the corner.
(A) back
(B) left
(C) third
(D) right

18. I play drums in the school _____.
Put a rubber _____ around the papers.
(A) chorus
(B) band
(C) stamp
(D) play

19. Use _____ to wrap the package.
I bought a new _____ at the music store.
(A) tape
(B) scissors
(C) elastic
(D) string

**GO ON ⇨**

# Test 2: Vocabulary (Form A), page 4

**Directions:** For questions 20–26 read each sentence. Find the word that fits in the blank. Then darken the circle for the correct answer.

**Sample D**

Mary is six years of _____.
- Ⓐ again
- Ⓑ age
- Ⓒ ago
- Ⓓ ask

20. Our family took a long _____ last summer.
- Ⓐ strip
- Ⓑ stop
- Ⓒ trip
- Ⓓ tribe

21. We went out on the lake in a _____.
- Ⓐ candle
- Ⓑ camp
- Ⓒ cannot
- Ⓓ canoe

22. Next _____ we're going to visit my grandmother.
- Ⓐ weep
- Ⓑ wheel
- Ⓒ weed
- Ⓓ week

23. Sally got a paper cut on her _____ .
- Ⓐ figure
- Ⓑ finger
- Ⓒ finish
- Ⓓ fight

24. The clouds looked _____ and gloomy.
- Ⓐ grade
- Ⓑ grain
- Ⓒ grape
- Ⓓ gray

25. The books are too _____ to put in a backpack.
- Ⓐ heat
- Ⓑ heavy
- Ⓒ health
- Ⓓ hear

26. July is a warm _____.
- Ⓐ moon
- Ⓑ mount
- Ⓒ month
- Ⓓ mouth

**STOP**

# Test 2: Vocabulary (Form B)

**Directions:** For questions 1–7 darken the circle for the word that has the *same* meaning or *almost the same* meaning as the underlined word.

### Sample A

<u>have</u> a bike
(A) play
(B) buy
(C) own
(D) start

**Time: 25 minutes**

1. <u>mend</u> the shirt
(A) cut
(B) repair
(C) wear
(D) wash

2. <u>harm</u> yourself
(A) help
(B) save
(C) sure
(D) hurt

3. <u>speak</u> softly
(A) talk
(B) read
(C) sing
(D) shout

4. <u>reply</u> to the question
(A) test
(B) bring
(C) answer
(D) ask

5. <u>shout</u> loudly
(A) sing
(B) yell
(C) wave
(D) tell

6. <u>main</u> idea
(A) important
(B) other
(C) my
(D) sure

7. <u>beneath</u> the desk
(A) behind
(B) between
(C) under
(D) over

**GO ON ⇨**

# Test 2: Vocabulary (Form B), page 2

**Directions:** For questions 8–14 darken the circle for the word that means the *opposite* of the underlined word.

**Sample B**

<u>easy</u> questions

Ⓐ simple
Ⓑ hard
Ⓒ silly
Ⓓ funny

8. <u>weak</u> ankle
   Ⓐ broken
   Ⓑ strong
   Ⓒ soft
   Ⓓ happy

9. <u>warm</u> weather
   Ⓐ rainy
   Ⓑ cool
   Ⓒ sunny
   Ⓓ clear

10. <u>shout</u> the answer
    Ⓐ call
    Ⓑ say
    Ⓒ write
    Ⓓ whisper

11. a <u>cheerful</u> story
    Ⓐ happy
    Ⓑ sad
    Ⓒ scary
    Ⓓ silly

12. an <u>expensive</u> toy
    Ⓐ cheap
    Ⓑ cheerful
    Ⓒ deep
    Ⓓ extra

13. <u>end</u> of the game
    Ⓐ rule
    Ⓑ score
    Ⓒ start
    Ⓓ time

14. <u>accept</u> the answer
    Ⓐ write
    Ⓑ reject
    Ⓒ tell
    Ⓓ give

**GO ON ⇨**

# Test 2: Vocabulary (Form B), page 3

**Directions:** For questions 15–21 read each sentence. Then darken the circle for the word that best completes each sentence.

### Sample C

My mother has a good _____ for fudge cake.
- (A) friend
- (B) dessert
- (C) recipe
- (D) reason

15. I took _____ with my new camera.
- (A) books
- (B) records
- (C) coins
- (D) pictures

16. The speaker stood on the _____.
- (A) platform
- (B) news
- (C) school
- (D) plant

17. Get off the bus at the next _____.
- (A) window
- (B) page
- (C) stop
- (D) cabin

18. I took a long _____ because I was so tired.
- (A) walk
- (B) dance
- (C) list
- (D) nap

19. Jerry collects _____ cars.
- (A) score
- (B) model
- (C) happy
- (D) animal

20. We made a _____ for dinner at the new restaurant.
- (A) mention
- (B) catcher
- (C) reservation
- (D) troop

21. Margie is a very _____ artist.
- (A) main
- (B) talented
- (C) talking
- (D) last

**GO ON ⇨**

# Test 2: Vocabulary (Form B), page 4

**Directions:** For questions 22–27 read the underlined phrases. Then darken the circle for the word that fits both meanings.

**Sample D**

used to shine floors
comes from a beehive

Ⓐ honey
Ⓑ soap
Ⓒ wax
Ⓓ comb

22. the opposite of *heavy*
    the opposite of *dark*
    Ⓐ weak
    Ⓑ gray
    Ⓒ thin
    Ⓓ light

23. the season after winter
    a coil made of metal
    Ⓐ spring
    Ⓑ summer
    Ⓒ wire
    Ⓓ fall

24. someone who cheers for a sports team
    something used to move air
    Ⓐ wind
    Ⓑ coach
    Ⓒ fan
    Ⓓ root

25. part of a pair for your feet
    to hit someone hard
    Ⓐ shoe
    Ⓑ sock
    Ⓒ slap
    Ⓓ glove

26. eat it with butter
    move on wheels
    Ⓐ bread
    Ⓑ skate
    Ⓒ drive
    Ⓓ roll

27. dates grow on this kind of tree
    a part of the hand
    Ⓐ oak
    Ⓑ finger
    Ⓒ palm
    Ⓓ nail

# Test 2: Vocabulary (Form C)

**Directions:** For questions 1–7 darken the circle for the word that means the *same* or *almost the same* as the underlined word.

**Sample A**

<u>giant</u> building
- Ⓐ good
- Ⓑ huge
- Ⓒ high
- Ⓓ wide

**Time: 25 minutes**

1. <u>traded</u> books
   - Ⓐ exchanged
   - Ⓑ read
   - Ⓒ collected
   - Ⓓ returned

2. favorite <u>melody</u>
   - Ⓐ hat
   - Ⓑ story
   - Ⓒ tune
   - Ⓓ thing

3. <u>snip</u> hair
   - Ⓐ set
   - Ⓑ cut
   - Ⓒ file
   - Ⓓ wave

4. <u>hammer</u> nails
   - Ⓐ buy
   - Ⓑ use
   - Ⓒ drop
   - Ⓓ pound

5. <u>unlock</u> the chest
   - Ⓐ open
   - Ⓑ cover
   - Ⓒ stuff
   - Ⓓ fill

6. <u>greet</u> the guests
   - Ⓐ invite
   - Ⓑ teach
   - Ⓒ treat
   - Ⓓ welcome

7. <u>delicious</u> cake
   - Ⓐ pretty
   - Ⓑ tasty
   - Ⓒ fancy
   - Ⓓ happy

**GO ON ⇨**

Name _____  Date _____

# Test 2: Vocabulary (Form C), page 2

**Directions:** For questions 8–14 darken the circle for the word or words that mean the *opposite* of the underlined word.

**Sample B**
<u>public</u> school
Ⓐ middle
Ⓑ high
Ⓒ open
Ⓓ private

8. <u>ancient</u> books
Ⓐ very new
Ⓑ very old
Ⓒ very torn
Ⓓ very fine

9. <u>darken</u> the room
Ⓐ brighten
Ⓑ paper
Ⓒ dim
Ⓓ fill

10. <u>arrive</u> on time
Ⓐ come
Ⓑ stay
Ⓒ leave
Ⓓ ask

11. <u>remember</u> the story
Ⓐ forget
Ⓑ tell
Ⓒ read
Ⓓ write

12. <u>rare</u> paintings
Ⓐ art
Ⓑ special
Ⓒ ordinary
Ⓓ oil

13. a <u>pleasant</u> scene
Ⓐ disagreeable
Ⓑ nice
Ⓒ happy
Ⓓ careless

14. the <u>upper</u> floor
Ⓐ fourth
Ⓑ top
Ⓒ high
Ⓓ lower

**GO ON ⇨**

# Test 2: Vocabulary (Form C), page 3

**Directions:** For questions 15–19 read each sentence. Then darken the circle for the word that best completes the sentence.

## Sample C

We were all _____ to Mimi's party.
Which word means that Mimi asked us to come to her party?
Ⓐ told
Ⓑ invited
Ⓒ taken
Ⓓ given

15. Our committee _____ the project last week.
Which word means that the project was finished?
Ⓐ started
Ⓑ began
Ⓒ took
Ⓓ completed

16. The _____ in Canada is cold in the winter.
Which word means the kind of weather?
Ⓐ climate
Ⓑ food
Ⓒ water
Ⓓ sun

17. Our coat _____ doesn't have enough hangers.
Which word means a place to hang clothes?
Ⓐ desk
Ⓑ dresser
Ⓒ closet
Ⓓ lamp

18. Were you able to _____ her name in the phone book?
Which word means to find?
Ⓐ locate
Ⓑ print
Ⓒ read
Ⓓ draw

19. You need a _____ to steer a canoe on the lake.
Which word means a kind of stick to use with a canoe?
Ⓐ bat
Ⓑ rod
Ⓒ paddle
Ⓓ basket

**GO ON ⇨**

# Test 2: Vocabulary (Form C), page 4

> **Directions:** For questions 20–24 read both sentences. Then darken the circle for the word that fits both sentences.
>
> **Sample D**
> Please ____ me that book.
> I hurt my ____ with the scissors.
> Ⓐ read
> Ⓑ sell
> Ⓒ hand
> Ⓓ give

**20.** Fill in the _____ under the word.
I wonder what it is like to go up in _____ .
Ⓐ dot
Ⓑ mountains
Ⓒ box
Ⓓ space

**21.** Vanessa loves to watch bubbles _____ in the air.
We built a beautiful _____ for the parade.
Ⓐ float
Ⓑ wagon
Ⓒ soar
Ⓓ stand

**22.** We're getting a new _____ in our kitchen.
A cork does not _____ in water.
Ⓐ table
Ⓑ light
Ⓒ sink
Ⓓ door

**23.** Our team needs to buy new _____ .
Did you see those _____ flying in the barn?
Ⓐ uniforms
Ⓑ bats
Ⓒ caps
Ⓓ flies

**24.** We put all the gifts in the _____ of the car.
It's interesting to watch an elephant use its _____.
Ⓐ back
Ⓑ trunk
Ⓒ seat
Ⓓ tusk

# Test 2: Vocabulary (Form D)

**Directions:** For questions 1–7 choose the word that should be added to each group of words. Then darken the circle for the correct answer.

## Sample A

red, black, purple,
- Ⓐ game
- Ⓑ brown
- Ⓒ book
- Ⓓ doll

**Time: 25 minutes**

1. shoes, socks, shirt,
   - Ⓐ hair
   - Ⓑ paper
   - Ⓒ spoon
   - Ⓓ dress

2. oranges, peaches, plums,
   - Ⓐ houses
   - Ⓑ rooms
   - Ⓒ days
   - Ⓓ apples

3. silk, wool, nylon,
   - Ⓐ cotton
   - Ⓑ wood
   - Ⓒ nails
   - Ⓓ gold

4. tennis, golf, soccer,
   - Ⓐ games
   - Ⓑ hockey
   - Ⓒ playground
   - Ⓓ score

5. pansies, lilacs, roses,
   - Ⓐ cherries
   - Ⓑ letters
   - Ⓒ boats
   - Ⓓ tulips

6. car, train, bus,
   - Ⓐ plane
   - Ⓑ farm
   - Ⓒ store
   - Ⓓ table

7. one, fifty, four,
   - Ⓐ song
   - Ⓑ pencil
   - Ⓒ sixteen
   - Ⓓ face

**GO ON ⇨**

# Test 2: Vocabulary (Form D), page 2

**Directions:** For questions 8–14 darken the circle for the word that means the *opposite* of the underlined word.

**Sample B**

young
- Ⓐ weak
- Ⓑ thin
- Ⓒ old
- Ⓓ small

**8.** after
- Ⓐ sooner
- Ⓑ later
- Ⓒ before
- Ⓓ earlier

**9.** quick
- Ⓐ still
- Ⓑ slow
- Ⓒ cross
- Ⓓ wise

**10.** absent
- Ⓐ present
- Ⓑ away
- Ⓒ returned
- Ⓓ gone

**11.** crooked
- Ⓐ straight
- Ⓑ sharp
- Ⓒ across
- Ⓓ path

**12.** lead
- Ⓐ children
- Ⓑ chase
- Ⓒ run
- Ⓓ follow

**13.** wise
- Ⓐ easy
- Ⓑ doctor
- Ⓒ foolish
- Ⓓ smart

**14.** war
- Ⓐ soldier
- Ⓑ flag
- Ⓒ peace
- Ⓓ strong

**GO ON ⇨**

# Test 2: Vocabulary (Form D), page 3

---

**Directions:** For questions 15–21 choose the word that tells about the underlined word. Then darken the circle for the correct answer.

**Sample C**

snow

Ⓐ warm
Ⓑ green
Ⓒ white
Ⓓ sharp

---

15. ice
    Ⓐ cold
    Ⓑ warm
    Ⓒ tall
    Ⓓ wide

16. fire
    Ⓐ cool
    Ⓑ hot
    Ⓒ good
    Ⓓ open

17. knife
    Ⓐ deep
    Ⓑ sharp
    Ⓒ dark
    Ⓓ loud

18. flower
    Ⓐ slow
    Ⓑ sleepy
    Ⓒ yellow
    Ⓓ rainy

19. story
    Ⓐ orange
    Ⓑ busy
    Ⓒ funny
    Ⓓ wide

20. building
    Ⓐ good
    Ⓑ clever
    Ⓒ tall
    Ⓓ helpless

21. sound
    Ⓐ loud
    Ⓑ speedy
    Ⓒ open
    Ⓓ narrow

**GO ON ⇨**

# Test 2: Vocabulary (Form D), page 4

---

**Directions:** For questions 22–28 choose the word that best completes the sentence. Darken the circle for the correct answer.

### Sample D

The letter was sent to the wrong _____.

- Ⓐ admire
- Ⓑ address
- Ⓒ advance
- Ⓓ admit

---

22. Our teacher kept our papers in her _____.
- Ⓐ debt
- Ⓑ delay
- Ⓒ depart
- Ⓓ desk

23. We learned about the stars and stripes on the _____.
- Ⓐ flat
- Ⓑ flame
- Ⓒ flag
- Ⓓ flash

24. The cup had a broken _____.
- Ⓐ harm
- Ⓑ handle
- Ⓒ harvest
- Ⓓ hardly

25. Nate showed us how to do the first _____.
- Ⓐ excellent
- Ⓑ example
- Ⓒ exact
- Ⓓ exit

26. The concert began at two _____.
- Ⓐ occupy
- Ⓑ octopus
- Ⓒ o'clock
- Ⓓ ocean

27. The cows were grazing in the _____.
- Ⓐ mean
- Ⓑ meadow
- Ⓒ metal
- Ⓓ middle

28. This summer my brother will go to _____.
- Ⓐ card
- Ⓑ camp
- Ⓒ castle
- Ⓓ cattle

**STOP**

# Test 3: Reading Comprehension (Form A)

**Directions:** For questions 1–3 choose the sentence that tells about the picture. Then darken the circle for the correct answer.

**Sample A**

Ⓐ The girl is going swimming.
Ⓑ The girl lost her sweater.
Ⓒ The girl is touching a spinner.
Ⓓ The girl is holding a puppy.

**Time: 30 minutes**

**1.**

Ⓐ The girl and boy are eating dinner.
Ⓑ The girl and boy are playing a game.
Ⓒ The girl and boy are setting the table.
Ⓓ The girl and boy are doing homework.

**2.**

Ⓐ He is painting the fence.
Ⓑ He is fixing the fence.
Ⓒ He is painting a picture.
Ⓓ His paintbrush is heavy.

**3.**

Ⓐ The girl is washing dishes.
Ⓑ The girl is shaking a jar of water.
Ⓒ The girl is making dinner.
Ⓓ The girl is spilling the water.

**GO ON ⇨**

# Test 3: Reading Comprehension (Form A), page 2

**Directions:** For questions 4–22 read the story or poem. Then darken the circle for the correct answer.

**Sample B**

### Dandelion Seeds

Dandelion seeds, dandelion seeds
Fly away, fly
Your soft, white hair will lift you
  so high
The wind will whirl you and
  twirl you
And spin you around
Then gently, so gently, you'll fall
  to the ground.

What will make the dandelion seeds fly?

Ⓐ the wind
Ⓑ the ground
Ⓒ spinning around
Ⓓ twirling

### Flowers in the Rain

Flowers standing in the rain
heads bent tightly together.
They never, never complain
about the drenching weather.

Soon the sun will shine and dry
their pretty flower faces.
Then they'll hold their heads
  up high
and shake off all rain's traces.

4. How do the flowers look when it is raining?
Ⓐ They stand straight and tall.
Ⓑ Their heads are bent over.
Ⓒ Their faces are pretty.
Ⓓ They smile at the sun.

5. Which is another word for *drenching*?
Ⓐ bending
Ⓑ shaking
Ⓒ shining
Ⓓ soaking

6. What makes the flowers hold their heads high?
Ⓐ the sun
Ⓑ rain's traces
Ⓒ drenching weather
Ⓓ pretty flower faces

**GO ON ⇨**

# Test 3: Reading Comprehension (Form A), page 3

Anita was excited! This was the day she had been waiting for. Her brothers had been practicing with her and giving her tips on pitching.

Her little-league coach told her that she was going to be the starting pitcher for the play-off game. She was so nervous that she could hardly eat breakfast. She gulped down her juice and cereal.

"Wish me luck," she said to her parents and brothers as she ran out the door. She wanted to talk to the coach before the rest of the team got on the bus.

Four hours later the team returned. Anita ran all the way home. She could hardly wait to tell her family the news about the game!

7. What position did Anita play for her team?
   Ⓐ catcher
   Ⓑ shortstop
   Ⓒ coach
   Ⓓ pitcher

8. How do you know that her brothers wanted her to do well?
   Ⓐ They practiced with her.
   Ⓑ They wished her luck.
   Ⓒ They ate breakfast together.
   Ⓓ They talked to the coach.

9. What do you think Anita's news was about the game?
   Ⓐ The bus got there on time.
   Ⓑ The coach let her get on the bus.
   Ⓒ They got back in four hours.
   Ⓓ Her team won.

10. Which could be a good title for this story?
    Ⓐ Anita Eats Breakfast
    Ⓑ Anita Pitches a Game
    Ⓒ Talking to the Coach
    Ⓓ Anita Practices with Her Brothers

# Test 3: Reading Comprehension (Form A), page 4

### The Flicker

The flicker is one of the most interesting birds. It is one of the largest members of the woodpecker family. It is about a foot long—a little larger than a robin. It has a brown back with black bars across the back. Its underparts are tan and marked with black dots. A large, black crescent can be seen across the flicker's breast. A smaller, bright scarlet crescent can be seen on its gray head.

When the flicker flies, you can see a large, white spot on the lower part of its back, but the feathers under the tail and wings are a golden yellow. Sometimes the flicker is called the "Golden-winged Woodpecker." Sometimes it is called "High-hole" because of its nest high up in a tree trunk.

Instead of liking the woods or forests, this woodpecker likes more open country. It can often be seen on the ground looking for ants, which are the flicker's favorite food. The flicker thumps on the ground with its curved bill. The ants rush out, and the flicker licks them up with its long tongue. The flicker also likes beetles, moths, butterflies, and all kinds of berries, including poison ivy berries. Farmers think that flickers are very helpful.

Flickers nest in any large hole they find in a tree, or they hollow out a home high up on a dead tree trunk as other woodpeckers do. They lay four to six shiny, white eggs. When the eggs are hatched, the parents feed the babies by thrusting their bills down the babies' throats to give them partly digested food.

# Test 3: Reading Comprehension (Form A), page 5

11. Which bird is almost as long as the flicker?
    Ⓐ woodpecker
    Ⓑ robin
    Ⓒ "Golden-wing"
    Ⓓ "High-hole"

12. Which word means *shaped like a new moon*?
    Ⓐ scarlet
    Ⓑ breast
    Ⓒ crescent
    Ⓓ thrusting

13. When will you see a large, white spot on the flicker's back?
    Ⓐ when it flies
    Ⓑ when it is on the ground
    Ⓒ when it is feeding its babies
    Ⓓ when its feathers are golden yellow

14. Why do farmers think that flickers are helpful?
    Ⓐ They live in dead trees.
    Ⓑ They like more open country.
    Ⓒ They eat insects that could harm plants.
    Ⓓ They have long tongues.

15. How do flickers get ants?
    Ⓐ They search the trees.
    Ⓑ They look in the woods.
    Ⓒ They thump on the ground with their bill.
    Ⓓ They wait for the ants to come to them.

16. What part of the flicker has black dots?
    Ⓐ wings
    Ⓑ back
    Ⓒ head
    Ⓓ underparts

17. Why is the flicker called the "Golden-winged Woodpecker?"
    Ⓐ It nests high up in a tree trunk.
    Ⓑ It has white spots on the lower parts of its back.
    Ⓒ The feathers under its tail and wings are golden yellow.
    Ⓓ You can see it on the ground.

18. How do baby flickers get their food?
    Ⓐ They search for berries.
    Ⓑ They search for ants.
    Ⓒ Their parents put food down the babies' throats.
    Ⓓ They eat beetles.

**GO ON ⇨**

# Test 3: Reading Comprehension (Form A), page 6

Roberto saw cattle in the meadow. He saw his grandfather working in the garden. Men were cutting hay in the field. In the yard he saw some hens and baby chicks.

**19.** Where was Roberto?
- Ⓐ in the city
- Ⓑ on a farm
- Ⓒ at school
- Ⓓ at the lake

The snowdrifts were deep, the wind was cold, and it was dark. Smoke curled out of the chimneys. Very few people were on the streets.

**20.** What time of year was it?
- Ⓐ summer
- Ⓑ winter
- Ⓒ spring
- Ⓓ fall

The doors closed with a bang, and the train started. It moved so quickly that Leo could hardly catch his breath. Leo didn't even hear what his father was saying.

**21.** Which word tells how the train was moving?
- Ⓐ smoothly
- Ⓑ quietly
- Ⓒ slowly
- Ⓓ swiftly

A young man in uniform put their luggage on a special cart. He led them to an elevator. They got off at the tenth floor, and the bellhop showed them to their room.

**22.** Where were these people?
- Ⓐ in a restaurant
- Ⓑ in a hotel
- Ⓒ in a garden
- Ⓓ in a theater

# Test 3: Reading Comprehension (Form B)

**Directions:** For questions 1–2 find the sentence that does not belong in each paragraph. Then darken the circle for the correct answer.

## Sample A

1. When the boy came to the huge stone in the road, he stopped. 2. "It's getting dark. 3. Someone might fall over this stone," he said to himself. 4. His shirt had blue stripes on it. 5. He decided to roll the stone out of the road.

Which sentence does not belong in the paragraph?

- Ⓐ Sentence 2
- Ⓑ Sentence 3
- Ⓒ Sentence 4
- Ⓓ Sentence 5

**Time: 30 minutes**

1. We had been waiting on the sidewalk for a long time. 2. My little sister got a new doll. 3. At last we heard a band playing. 4. Soon the band appeared. 5. Then the beautiful floats came behind the band.

1. Which sentence does not belong in this paragraph?
- Ⓐ Sentence 1
- Ⓑ Sentence 2
- Ⓒ Sentence 3
- Ⓓ Sentence 4

1. After the flood two hundred people from another state came to help. 2. They brought blankets and clothing. 3. They brought food for everyone. 4. It was springtime. 5. They brought toys for the children.

2. Which sentence does not belong in this paragraph?
- Ⓐ Sentence 5
- Ⓑ Sentence 4
- Ⓒ Sentence 3
- Ⓓ Sentnece 2

**GO ON ⇨**

# Test 3: Reading Comprehension (Form B), page 2

**Directions:** For questions 3–22 read the story or poem. Then darken the circle for the correct answer.

## Sample B

Elvin is getting off the school bus. He is standing on the right side of the exit door. He holds onto the rail until the bus comes to a full stop.

What is this paragraph about?
- Ⓐ safety on the bus
- Ⓑ working on the bus
- Ⓒ playing on the bus
- Ⓓ reading on the bus

The pans with loaves in them move away on a belt to the steam box. The steam box is really a low room. It is made very hot by steam pipes. As the loaves move slowly through the steam box, the dough gets lighter and lighter. Soon it is ready to be baked. The loaves are moved from the steam box into the oven where they are baked.

3. What makes the dough get lighter?
- Ⓐ the steam
- Ⓑ a belt
- Ⓒ a box
- Ⓓ an oven

4. What is being baked?
- Ⓐ bread
- Ⓑ cookies
- Ⓒ muffins
- Ⓓ pies

5. You can tell that this takes place in a _____.
- Ⓐ house
- Ⓑ store
- Ⓒ school
- Ⓓ bakery

6. A good title for this story could be _____.
- Ⓐ Loaf Pans
- Ⓑ Steam Boxes and Ovens
- Ⓒ How Bread Is Baked
- Ⓓ Hot Steam Pipes

**GO ON ⇒**

# Test 3: Reading Comprehension (Form B), page 3

### If I Were Bigger

If I were bigger
I'd climb up that tree
And sit way up on top
Then I'd look down and see
The world all around
Buildings and tiny houses
So close to the ground
I'd see cars and trucks go
    whizzing by
Some go so fast, they almost
    fly
And I would smile
As I sat up so high
And in a little while
I'd touch the sky.

7. Who is the speaker in this poem?
   Ⓐ a man
   Ⓑ a woman
   Ⓒ a child
   Ⓓ a pet

8. Why would the buildings and houses look tiny?
   Ⓐ The speaker is up very high.
   Ⓑ They are close to the ground.
   Ⓒ They are near the tree.
   Ⓓ The speaker is bigger.

9. What will it be impossible for the speaker to do?
   Ⓐ watch cars whiz by
   Ⓑ see the world all around
   Ⓒ touch the sky
   Ⓓ climb very high

10. Which could be another title for this poem?
   Ⓐ Touching the Sky
   Ⓑ View From a Treetop
   Ⓒ Cars Whiz By
   Ⓓ Climbing Trees

GO ON ⇨

# Test 3: Reading Comprehension (Form B), page 4

Getting enough drinking water and water to put out fires was a serious problem for the people of New York City in 1774. "Tea Water" men had licenses to cart and sell water from pure springs to people in the city, but this wasn't enough water.

A man named Christopher Colles came up with a plan for a waterworks. His idea was to build a covered reservoir, or artificial lake, to store water. From the reservoir he wanted to send pure water through thirteen miles of hollowed-out log pipes. His plan was to convey water to every street and lane in New York City with pipes placed every one hundred yards. Mr. Colles assured everyone that they would be able to draw water at any time of day or night.

The plan was for the water pump to pump two hundred gallons of water at a rate of fifty-two feet per minute. The city agreed to follow this plan, but before work could be started, the Revolutionary

War broke out and the need for clean water was forgotten for a while.

11. What problem did the people of New York City have?
    Ⓐ building water pumps
    Ⓑ licensing "Tea Water" men
    Ⓒ getting pure drinking water
    Ⓓ building a reservoir

12. How did the people of New York City get clean drinking water in 1774?
    Ⓐ They pumped it from pure springs.
    Ⓑ They bought it from "Tea Water" men.
    Ⓒ They built a huge pump.
    Ⓓ They covered the reservoir.

# Test 3: Reading Comprehension (Form B), page 5

**13.** What does the word *convey* mean in this story?
- Ⓐ lift
- Ⓑ drink
- Ⓒ pure
- Ⓓ carry

**14.** How much water did Mr. Colles say the waterworks would pump per minute?
- Ⓐ two hundred gallons
- Ⓑ a hundred yards
- Ⓒ fifty-two gallons
- Ⓓ thirteen miles

**15.** Why was the plan forgotten for a while?
- Ⓐ It cost too much money.
- Ⓑ The log pipes broke.
- Ⓒ The Revolutionary War broke out.
- Ⓓ It was a serious problem.

**16.** Where did Mr. Colles plan to send the water?
- Ⓐ to a waterworks
- Ⓑ to every street and lane in the city
- Ⓒ to a reservoir
- Ⓓ to a large pump

**17.** What was going to be the most special thing about the waterworks?
- Ⓐ People could get water any time of day or night.
- Ⓑ It would have thirteen miles of hollowed-out logs.
- Ⓒ It would have a large pump.
- Ⓓ It would pump two hundred gallons of water.

**18.** What do you think happened after the Revolutionary War?
- Ⓐ They built the waterworks.
- Ⓑ Mr. Colles changed his mind.
- Ⓒ The reservoir couldn't be built.
- Ⓓ There were not enough logs.

**GO ON ⇨**

# Test 3: Reading Comprehension (Form B), page 6

One morning there was frost. Little white splinters of ice stuck to every green blade, every leaf, and every plant in the garden. That very day the leaves on the tomatoes, beans, and other plants in the garden withered and turned black. The leaves on the tree had already begun to turn yellow and red. Now they changed much faster. It seemed almost like a yellow and red world.

**19.** What season is this story about?
(A) summer
(B) fall
(C) winter
(D) spring

**20.** What is another word for *withered*?
(A) wintered
(B) tore
(C) slipped
(D) dried

**21.** What made the plants turn black?
(A) the frost
(B) the green blades
(C) the yellow and red leaves
(D) the early morning

**22.** How many different colors are named in this story?
(A) five
(B) two
(C) four
(D) three

STOP

# Test 3: Reading Comprehension (Form C)

**Directions:** For questions 1–2 choose a title for each paragraph. Then darken the circle for the correct answer.

### Sample A

Dean had heard stories about elves, but he had never known that they were such tiny creatures. The elf he saw had an old, wrinkled face. He was dressed in a black coat, knee pants, and a broad-brimmed black hat. He was looking at a toy he was making on the workbench. He didn't know that Dean was watching him.

Which is a good title for this paragraph?
- Ⓐ Stories About Elves
- Ⓑ Dean Sees an Elf
- Ⓒ Making Toys
- Ⓓ The Young Elf

**Time: 30 minutes**

1. Most beavers live in lodges that are built in pools in small  streams and ponds. The lodges are made of sticks and mud. Some of them are several feet high. A part of the beaver lodge always stays above the water, but the entrance is always covered by water.
- Ⓐ A Beaver Lodge
- Ⓑ How Beavers Cut Down Trees
- Ⓒ Tall Beaver Lodges
- Ⓓ Using Sticks and Mud

2. In early summer the sheep are washed in clean water. As soon as the wool is dry, it is cut from the backs of the sheep with heavy shears. The wool from each sheep sticks together like a mat and is called *fleece*. The sheep grow new wool to keep them warm all winter.
- Ⓐ Keeping Sheep Warm
- Ⓑ Fleece and Mat
- Ⓒ Washing Sheep
- Ⓓ Cutting Wool from Sheep

**GO ON ⇨**

# Test 3: Reading Comprehension (Form C), page 2

**Directions:** For questions 3–22 read each story. Then darken the circle for the correct answer.

### Sample B

Jay went to the store to buy bread. He had two dollars in his pocket. He used the money to pay for the bread.

What did Jay have in his pocket?
- Ⓐ bread
- Ⓑ coins
- Ⓒ two dollars
- Ⓓ paper

Rice is grown in countries in Asia and in the United States. The rice in Asia is planted in a field that looks like a big mud pie. Each young rice plant is set into its muddy bed by hand. What a squashy, muddy feeling the rice farmers must have as they walk barefoot up and down the rows setting out the plants! This big mud pie is called a rice paddy.

In the United States, rice is planted the same way that wheat and other grains are planted. The land is plowed and rolled before the rice plants are set in it.

3. What is the main idea of this story?
- Ⓐ rice planting in Asia
- Ⓑ rice planting in the United States
- Ⓒ comparing rice planting in Asia with rice planting in the United States
- Ⓓ walking barefoot in a rice field

4. In what kind of land is rice planted in Asia?
- Ⓐ wet, muddy land
- Ⓑ high, dry land
- Ⓒ plowed fields
- Ⓓ wheat fields

5. Why do Asian farmers walk barefoot in rice fields?
- Ⓐ They have no shoes.
- Ⓑ The fields are wet.
- Ⓒ The plants are very young.
- Ⓓ They like the squashy feeling.

6. To what does the writer compare a rice paddy?
- Ⓐ a mud pie
- Ⓑ a plowed field
- Ⓒ muddy hands
- Ⓓ planting fields

**GO ON ⇨**

Name _____ Date _____

# Test 3: Reading Comprehension (Form C), page 3

From early June until August you can find the wild rose dotting meadows, pastures, and rocky hillsides. It has a lovely, delicate fragrance and is used to make many fine perfumes. Probably the most common wild rose is the Pasture Rose. Another variety is the Sweetbrier, which many people consider to be one of the loveliest of all roadside flowers. Its leaves have a fragrant smell that reminds people of apple blossoms. Wild roses have only single flowers, not the double flowers you see on cultivated, or store, roses.

7. What is meant by a cultivated rose?
   A Someone planted it and watched it grow.
   B It is grown in a field.
   C It doesn't have double flowers.
   D It has a lovely fragrance.

8. How is a wild rose different from a cultivated rose?
   A It smells like apple blossoms.
   B It is used to make perfume.
   C It doesn't have double flowers.
   D You can buy it in a store.

9. Which is the most common of the wild roses?
   A Pasture Rose
   B Sweetbrier Rose
   C Rocky Hill Rose
   D Meadow Rose

10. Where does the Sweetbrier Rose usually grow?
    A in meadows
    B in rocky hillsides
    C in stores
    D along roadsides

# Test 3: Reading Comprehension (Form C), page 4

Years ago three men at the South Pole made a new kind of car to travel over ice and snow. They called it a snowmobile. Everyone in Antarctica was excited when the men decided to try their new snowmobile.

There were no roads to follow over the fields deep with snow. The snowmobile had hard work to do. Sometimes it had to climb over great blocks of ice. Sometimes it had to go through huge piles of snow.

The snowmobile ran well for two days. It sped over the ice and snow, and the men were pleased. They thought that they had found a better way to travel than by using a slow dog team. But on the third day when they had gone about eighty miles, the snowmobile ran into a deep snowdrift. It groaned and choked and finally stopped. The men tried to pull it out, but the back end was broken by the snow. The nearest gas stations and garages were more than a thousand miles away. They had to leave the snowmobile in the snowdrift and walk home. It was bitter cold and snowing hard. It took them several days to get home.

Today snowmobiles are very popular in areas where there is a lot of snow. People use them for recreation, as well as to travel over snow-covered roads. In areas very far north, dog teams are still used, too.

Heel!

**GO ON ⇨**

# Test 3: Reading Comprehension (Form C), page 5

**11.** Why were people excited about the snowmobile?

Ⓐ The dogs were getting too tired.

Ⓑ They wanted to invent new things.

Ⓒ They thought it would be faster than a dog team.

Ⓓ They wanted to build roads.

**12.** How many days did the snowmobile run well?

Ⓐ two days

Ⓑ three days

Ⓒ several days

Ⓓ four days

**13.** How many miles did the men have to walk back?

Ⓐ a thousand miles

Ⓑ one hundred miles

Ⓒ eighty miles

Ⓓ two miles

**14.** What happened on the third day?

Ⓐ The snowmobile went over blocks of ice.

Ⓑ The snowmobile went through huge piles of snow.

Ⓒ The snowmobile broke.

Ⓓ There were no gas stations or garages.

**15.** Why wasn't the snowmobile useful in Antarctica?

Ⓐ The roads were rough.

Ⓑ There were no garages in Antarctica.

Ⓒ The snow was soft.

Ⓓ The snowdrifts were too deep.

**16.** What kind of power did the men probably use for the snowmobile?

Ⓐ electric

Ⓑ wind

Ⓒ gasoline

Ⓓ coal

**17.** A good title for this story could be _____.

Ⓐ The First Snowmobile

Ⓑ No More Dog Teams

Ⓒ A Long, Snowy Walk

Ⓓ Snowmobiles for Recreation

**18.** What kind of transportation did the men probably use the next time they had to go on a long trip?

Ⓐ another snowmobile

Ⓑ a horse and buggy

Ⓒ a dogsled

Ⓓ snow shoes

**GO ON ⇨**

# Test 3: Reading Comprehension (Form C), page 6

Just imagine! If big rocks had not been broken into little bits, we would not have any food to eat. That is because all the soil on our Earth—the dirt in which we plant flowers and vegetables and grain—is formed largely from rocks that have been crushed by wind, rain, and storms. Of course many other things are mixed with the ground-up rocks to make rich soil. It took hundreds of thousands of years to make our soil.

Some soil is full of pebbles that are larger than grains of sand. This soil is called gravel. Other soil is sandy. Some other soil, called clay, is made up of bits even smaller than sand. These bits are so small that you can hardly see them.

19. How is sand formed?
    Ⓐ from gravel
    Ⓑ from clay
    Ⓒ from pebbles
    Ⓓ from rocks that have been crushed

20. What do we call pebbles that are larger than grains of sand?
    Ⓐ sandy
    Ⓑ gravel
    Ⓒ rocks
    Ⓓ clay

21. What is clay made of?
    Ⓐ broken rocks
    Ⓑ things mixed with ground-up rock
    Ⓒ bits even smaller than sand
    Ⓓ gravel

22. Why do people want to take care of soil?
    Ⓐ They don't like it when the wind blows.
    Ⓑ It takes hundreds of thousands of years to make soil.
    Ⓒ There is too much gravel.
    Ⓓ They want to make a lot of clay.

STOP

# Test 3: Reading Comprehension (Form D)

**Directions:** For questions 1–3 decide which sentence tells about the picture. Then darken the circle for the correct answer.

**Sample A**

Ⓐ The girls are going for a walk.

Ⓑ The girls are dancing to the radio music.

Ⓒ The girls are in school.

Ⓓ The girls are jogging in the park.

**Time: 30 minutes**

**1.**

Ⓐ The woman is ironing the clothes.

Ⓑ The woman is cleaning her house.

Ⓒ The woman is washing the clothes.

Ⓓ The woman is finished

**2.**

Ⓐ The children are listening to a story.

Ⓑ The teacher wants the children to sit down.

Ⓒ The magician is doing tricks for the children.

Ⓓ The children are getting ready for school.

**3.**

Ⓐ The puppy is running away from the boy.

Ⓑ The boy doesn't want the puppy to come to him.

Ⓒ The puppy is jumping on the boy's lap.

Ⓓ The boy wants the puppy to run to him.

**GO ON ⇨**

# Test 3: Reading Comprehension (Form D), page 2

**Directions:** For questions 4–23 read each story or poem. Then darken the circle for the correct answer.

## Sample B

Passenger trains in the United States are carrying fewer people as air travel grows. At one time, travel by train was the fastest and easiest way to travel long distances.

Why are passenger trains carrying fewer people?
- Ⓐ They can't go long distances.
- Ⓑ They're not easy to travel on.
- Ⓒ Travel by train was the fastest.
- Ⓓ More people are traveling by plane.

Paint is a material used to cover or decorate walls and objects. It is a mixture of powder and liquid. The powder may be white or another color, while the liquid has no color and may be oil or water.

Paint has been used through the ages. Cave dwellers ground plants and clay into colored powder, added water, and then painted pictures on cave walls. The ancient Egyptians taught the Romans how to make paints. Later, paint was used on churches, buildings, and houses. American settlers made paint by mixing water with coffee grounds, eggs, and milk. In the late 1860s, factories began to make paint.

Today there are paints for cement, boats, and wood, as well as fireproof and rustproof paint. There are even poison paints to keep insects from eating wood.

Different tools are used for spreading paint. Children use their hands for finger painting. Artists use paintbrushes, as do housepainters. Housepainters also use paint rollers. Spray cans are the latest way to cover walls or other things with paint.

**GO ON ⇨**

# Test 3: Reading Comprehension (Form D), page 3

4. Which part of paint has no color?
   - Ⓐ powder
   - Ⓑ liquid
   - Ⓒ cement
   - Ⓓ clay

5. What does the author want you to know about paint?
   - Ⓐ It looks pretty on the wall.
   - Ⓑ Artists use it.
   - Ⓒ It can have many colors.
   - Ⓓ It has been used through the ages.

6. Who taught the Romans how to use paints?
   - Ⓐ ancient Egyptians
   - Ⓑ American settlers
   - Ⓒ cave dwellers
   - Ⓓ housepainters

7. What did American settlers use for liquid in their paint?
   - Ⓐ dirt
   - Ⓑ oil
   - Ⓒ water
   - Ⓓ coffee grounds

8. What does *fireproof paint* mean?
   - Ⓐ You can paint something with fire.
   - Ⓑ You cannot start a fire with it.
   - Ⓒ It will not burn if there is a fire.
   - Ⓓ It will burn easily.

9. What tools do children use when they are painting on paper?
   - Ⓐ rollers
   - Ⓑ fingers
   - Ⓒ stones
   - Ⓓ cement

10. Which is a good title for this story?
   - Ⓐ Painting Through the Ages
   - Ⓑ A New Kind of Paint
   - Ⓒ The Beginning of Paint Factories
   - Ⓓ All Kinds of Painting Tools

11. Why do you need liquid for paint?
   - Ⓐ It is colorless.
   - Ⓑ It is oily.
   - Ⓒ It helps spread the paint.
   - Ⓓ It can be used in a spray can.

**GO ON ⇨**

# Test 3: Reading Comprehension (Form D), page 4

**Ready or Not**

The sky sends different messages
a chill wind is in the air
Darkness comes so soon

Just a few scarlet leaves hang on
here and there a splash of gold
brightens a dark patch of earth

The mood of the world is serious
   now
People look out at tree skeletons
and snowdrifts
Waiting for spring.

12. What kind of message is the
    sky sending?
    Ⓐ Get ready for rain.
    Ⓑ Springtime is here.
    Ⓒ Winter is coming.
    Ⓓ The days are getting
       warmer.

13. Why do the trees look like
    skeletons?
    Ⓐ They're ready for
       Halloween.
    Ⓑ Their leaves are gone.
    Ⓒ They have some scarlet
       leaves.
    Ⓓ Darkness comes so soon.

14. Why does the poet call this
    poem "Ready or Not"?
    Ⓐ Winter will be here even if
       you're not ready for it.
    Ⓑ You can play Hide and Go
       Seek.
    Ⓒ The wind is chilly.
    Ⓓ You have to look at
       snowdrifts.

15. What is the "splash of gold"
    the poet talks about?
    Ⓐ someone's gold jewelry
    Ⓑ a gold painting
    Ⓒ some gold-colored leaves
    Ⓓ a can of gold paint

**GO ON ⇨**

# Test 3: Reading Comprehension (Form D), page 5

Many people travel to the Black Hills of South Dakota to see a magnificent sight. Carved into the side of Mount Rushmore are the faces of four American Presidents. They are George Washington, Thomas Jefferson, Theodore Roosevelt, and Abraham Lincoln. Each of these carvings stands sixty feet tall and can be seen from sixty miles away.

Gutzon Borglum, the sculptor, began carving the stone faces in 1927. But before he could even start, tons of stone had to be blasted away from the side of the mountain. It took fourteen years to finish the project. Unfortunately, Borglum died in 1941 when the project was almost finished. His son Lincoln finished the job.

16. Who carved the faces on Mount Rushmore?
    Ⓐ Thomas Jefferson
    Ⓑ Abraham Lincoln
    Ⓒ George Washington
    Ⓓ Gutzon Borglum

17. Why don't travelers have to get very close to the mountain?
    Ⓐ There are too many stones in the way.
    Ⓑ The faces can be seen from sixty miles away.
    Ⓒ It is too dangerous.
    Ⓓ The faces are not finished.

18. Which statement about this article is not true?
    Ⓐ Lincoln Borglum finished the job for his father.
    Ⓑ Mount Rushmore is in South Dakota.
    Ⓒ Each President's face is sixty feet tall.
    Ⓓ Gutzon Borglum finished the project in less than fourteen years.

19. Which is a good title for this article?
    Ⓐ Presidents on Mount Rushmore
    Ⓑ Blasting a Mountainside
    Ⓒ Stone Mountain
    Ⓓ The Black Hills

# Test 3: Reading Comprehension (Form D), page 6

To the Editor:

I think our school district should have year-round schools. I hope you will write an article in your paper about year-round schools. Year-round schools are better for students' learning. There are shorter breaks, so students don't have to do so much review. After short vacations, teachers can start to teach us more new things.

My parents think that year-round schools would be good for everyone. They said that if our school starts a pilot program with kids who really want to try it, they will sign me up. That's why I want you to write about year-round schools. If you do, a lot of people might be interested in trying it out.

Yours truly,

Juanita Sanchez

20. What does Juanita think about year-round schools?
    Ⓐ She is in favor of them.
    Ⓑ She is against them.
    Ⓒ She would never go to a year-round school.
    Ⓓ She doesn't agree with her parents.

21. What does the word *pilot* mean in this article?
    Ⓐ airplane flyer
    Ⓑ manage
    Ⓒ steer
    Ⓓ trial test

22. What is one reason why Juanita thinks that year-round schools would be good?
    Ⓐ Students wouldn't have to do so much review.
    Ⓑ Vacations would be better.
    Ⓒ Teachers like it better.
    Ⓓ The newspaper can write about it.

23. What is Juanita willing to do?
    Ⓐ study harder
    Ⓑ learn better
    Ⓒ help her parents
    Ⓓ be part of a pilot program

# Test 4: Spelling (Form A)

**Directions:** For questions 1–7 read each sentence. Then darken the circle for the correctly spelled word that fits the sentence.

**Sample**

We live on planet _____.

Ⓐ Erth
Ⓑ Eirth
Ⓒ Eurth
Ⓓ Earth

**Time: 10 minutes**

1. Mrs. Ferris is our school crossing _____.
   Ⓐ gaurd
   Ⓑ guard
   Ⓒ gard
   Ⓓ guarde

2. My grandfather is _____ years old!
   Ⓐ nintey
   Ⓑ ninetey
   Ⓒ ninty
   Ⓓ ninety

3. Snow White spoke to the _____.
   Ⓐ mirror
   Ⓑ mirrer
   Ⓒ mirrur
   Ⓓ miror

4. Last _____ we went to the zoo.
   Ⓐ Thersday
   Ⓑ Thursday
   Ⓒ Thuersday
   Ⓓ Thuresday

5. _____ turn is it to serve snacks?
   Ⓐ Who's
   Ⓑ Whoos
   Ⓒ Whose
   Ⓓ Whoose

6. Our scout _____ always has good ideas.
   Ⓐ leder
   Ⓑ leadder
   Ⓒ leider
   Ⓓ leader

7. What is the _____ between these two books?
   Ⓐ difference
   Ⓑ diffrence
   Ⓒ diffrince
   Ⓓ diference

**STOP**

Name _____  Date _____

# Test 4: Spelling (Form B)

**Directions:** For questions 1–7 darken the circle for the word that is *not* spelled correctly. Darken the circle for *No mistakes* if there are <u>no</u> spelling errors.

**Sample**
Ⓐ circle
Ⓑ about
Ⓒ meny
Ⓓ No mistakes

**Time: 10 minutes**

1. Ⓐ sometimes
   Ⓑ ghost
   Ⓒ travel
   Ⓓ No mistakes

2. Ⓐ jelley
   Ⓑ voice
   Ⓒ around
   Ⓓ No mistakes

3. Ⓐ steel
   Ⓑ puzzel
   Ⓒ cover
   Ⓓ No mistakes

4. Ⓐ adress
   Ⓑ surprise
   Ⓒ under
   Ⓓ No mistakes

5. Ⓐ elephant
   Ⓑ choose
   Ⓒ thirstey
   Ⓓ No mistakes

6. Ⓐ sail
   Ⓑ every
   Ⓒ friend
   Ⓓ No mistakes

7. Ⓐ foure
   Ⓑ repair
   Ⓒ always
   Ⓓ No mistakes

**STOP**

Name _____ Date _____

# Test 4: Spelling (Form C)

**Directions:** For questions 1–9 read each sentence. If one of the underlined words is misspelled, darken the circle for that word. If all of the words are correct, then darken the circle for *No mistake*.

**Sample**

We had to <u>trim</u> the <u>branchis</u> on the <u>maple</u> tree. <u>No mistake</u>
    Ⓐ          Ⓑ         Ⓒ        Ⓓ

**Time: 10 minutes**

1. We are <u>planning</u> to <u>climb</u> that <u>mountin</u>. <u>No mistake</u>
        Ⓐ         Ⓑ       Ⓒ       Ⓓ

2. Everyone <u>laughed</u> at the <u>funny</u> <u>story</u>. <u>No mistake</u>
         Ⓐ          Ⓑ   Ⓒ     Ⓓ

3. Sara <u>chose</u> the <u>tinyest</u> <u>earrings</u> for Lila. <u>No mistake</u>
      Ⓐ        Ⓑ    Ⓒ          Ⓓ

4. That <u>certinaly</u> was a <u>juicy</u> <u>pear</u>! <u>No mistake</u>
      Ⓐ         Ⓑ  Ⓒ    Ⓓ

5. Mom <u>always</u> <u>wears</u> an <u>aprin</u> when she cooks. <u>No mistake</u>
       Ⓐ     Ⓑ     Ⓒ             Ⓓ

6. <u>Potatoes</u> are a <u>starchy</u> <u>vegtible</u>. <u>No mistake</u>
   Ⓐ          Ⓑ    Ⓒ     Ⓓ

7. Do you like <u>whole</u> <u>wheet</u> <u>bread</u>? <u>No mistake</u>
           Ⓐ    Ⓑ   Ⓒ      Ⓓ

8. Use <u>boiling</u> <u>water</u> to <u>prepair</u> tea. <u>No mistake</u>
     Ⓐ    Ⓑ     Ⓒ        Ⓓ

9. Don't <u>lean</u> <u>against</u> that <u>shelf</u>. <u>No mistake</u>
     Ⓐ    Ⓑ      Ⓒ    Ⓓ

Name _____  Date _____

# Test 4: Spelling (Form D)

**Directions:** For questions 1–7 read each sentence. Then darken the circle for the correctly spelled word that fits the sentence.

**Sample**

I _____ do my homework in the afternoon.

Ⓐ allways
Ⓑ always
Ⓒ alwayz
Ⓓ allwayz

**Time: 10 minutes**

1. Is that _____ new jacket?
   Ⓐ yore
   Ⓑ you're
   Ⓒ your
   Ⓓ youre

2. Our new _____ comes from Alaska.
   Ⓐ neighbor
   Ⓑ neighber
   Ⓒ nayghbor
   Ⓓ nieghbor

3. How many _____ belong to that club?
   Ⓐ wimmen
   Ⓑ womin
   Ⓒ women
   Ⓓ wommen

4. _____ new car is light blue.
   Ⓐ They're
   Ⓑ Their
   Ⓒ There
   Ⓓ Thier

5. Wash your hands with _____.
   Ⓐ soup
   Ⓑ sope
   Ⓒ soape
   Ⓓ soap

6. I have to return my _____ books.
   Ⓐ libary
   Ⓑ liberry
   Ⓒ library
   Ⓓ librery

7. Next _____ is a holiday.
   Ⓐ Tusday
   Ⓑ tuesday
   Ⓒ Tuesday
   Ⓓ Tuseday

**STOP**

Name _____ Date _____

# Test 5: Language Mechanics (Form A)

**Directions:** For questions 1–3 read each sentence. Then darken the circle for the word that needs a capital letter. If no capital letter is needed, darken the circle for *None*.

**Sample A**

Ms. regan is my music teacher. None
  Ⓐ          Ⓑ      Ⓒ          Ⓓ

**Time: 15 minutes**

**1.** My grandmother lives in westbury, Iowa. None
                  Ⓐ                    Ⓑ    Ⓒ    Ⓓ

**2.** Turn right on Mulberry Street. None
       Ⓐ          Ⓑ          Ⓒ     Ⓓ

**3.** We visited the museum of Modern Art. None
        Ⓐ          Ⓑ          Ⓒ          Ⓓ

**Directions:** For questions 4–6 read each sentence. Then darken the circle for the correct punctuation mark. If no other punctuation is needed, darken the circle for *None*.

**Sample B**

Are you Fran's brother
Ⓐ   ,
Ⓑ   ?
Ⓒ   !
Ⓓ   None

**4.** How old is your sister?
Ⓐ   .
Ⓑ   ,
Ⓒ   !
Ⓓ   None

**5.** Don't walk in the street
Ⓐ   !
Ⓑ   ?
Ⓒ   ,
Ⓓ   None

**6.** I like cookies but I like ice cream better.
Ⓐ   "
Ⓑ   ,
Ⓒ   ?
Ⓓ   None

**GO ON ⇨**

**71**

# Test 5: Language Mechanics (Form A), page 2

**Directions:** For questions 7–12 read each sentence. Then darken the circle for the sentence that has correct capitalization and punctuation.

**Sample C**

Ⓐ We start school in september

Ⓑ Her family is going to New York.

Ⓒ The american flag was raised on the flag pole.

Ⓓ Did you find my new pen

7. Ⓐ Can you help me with my spelling

Ⓑ Don't go near the fire!

Ⓒ Story hour will be held on Wednesday

Ⓓ My cousin Jeff moved to ohio.

8. Ⓐ Please, turn down the radio?

Ⓑ why can't you come with me?

Ⓒ Which is your favorite TV program?

Ⓓ Isn't that dr. Fine?

9. Ⓐ I shop at the Pretty Pottery Palace.

Ⓑ Mr. mandel is a good science teacher.

Ⓒ When will you be finished with that book.

Ⓓ I'm really tired today,

10. Ⓐ Dr. Seuss wrote *the cat in the hat*.

Ⓑ The olympics were held in Atlanta Georgia

Ⓒ My friend lives in Austin, Texas.

Ⓓ Where are you going

11. Ⓐ Her birthday is April 7!

Ⓑ Watch out!

Ⓒ I'll talk to you later!

Ⓓ I'd like to go to the store!

12. Ⓐ Who forgot to close the door?

Ⓑ i think I'll buy a new hat?

Ⓒ The month of november has many holidays

Ⓓ They arrived too late?

# Test 5: Language Mechanics (Form B)

**Directions:** For questions 1–7 darken the circle for the line that has a capitalization error. Darken the circle for *No mistakes* if the sentence is correct.

**Sample A**
Ⓐ Gina goes to
Ⓑ dancing school
Ⓒ every wednesday afternoon.
Ⓓ No mistakes

**Time: 15 minutes**

1. Ⓐ Next week my cousins
   Ⓑ Raoul and julia
   Ⓒ are coming to visit us.
   Ⓓ No mistakes

2. Ⓐ St. John, New brunswick,
   Ⓑ is where you can see
   Ⓒ the Reversing Falls.
   Ⓓ No mistakes

3. Ⓐ Who is your favorite
   Ⓑ author? Mine is
   Ⓒ Dr. Seuss.
   Ⓓ No mistakes

4. Ⓐ We visited the
   Ⓑ Grand Canyon in
   Ⓒ arizona last summer.
   Ⓓ No mistakes

5. Ⓐ My friend Dorrie Costello
   Ⓑ will be nine years old
   Ⓒ on her next Birthday.
   Ⓓ No mistakes

6. Ⓐ Rosita and i will
   Ⓑ help Ms. Seng
   Ⓒ unpack the new library
      books.
   Ⓓ No mistakes

7. Ⓐ My father is going
   Ⓑ to Stockton. he needs to
   Ⓒ buy computer paper.
   Ⓓ No mistakes

**GO ON ⇨**

# Test 5: Language Mechanics (Form B), page 2

**Directions:** For questions 8–14 darken the circle for the line that has a punctuation error. Darken the circle for *No mistakes* if the sentence has no errors.

**Sample B**
Ⓐ Ian said, "Let's
Ⓑ play a game of
Ⓒ basketball after school.
Ⓓ No mistakes

8. Ⓐ My aunt is coming
   Ⓑ to visit. I want to
   Ⓒ show her my school.
   Ⓓ No mistakes

9. Ⓐ My mother always uses
   Ⓑ apples, bananas peaches,
   Ⓒ and oranges in fruit salad.
   Ⓓ No mistakes

10. Ⓐ Mr. Chan asked, "Who
    Ⓑ wants to try to do this
    Ⓒ science experiment?"
    Ⓓ No mistakes

11. Ⓐ When is your sister
    Ⓑ going to start taking
    Ⓒ voice lessons.
    Ⓓ No mistakes

12. Ⓐ Mrs. Smiths garden
    Ⓑ is the prettiest one
    Ⓒ on our street.
    Ⓓ No mistakes

13. Ⓐ Dear Tina
    Ⓑ Thank you for the
    Ⓒ set of watercolors.
    Ⓓ No mistakes

14. Ⓐ Terri got a really
    Ⓑ cute poodle for her birthday.
    Ⓒ She named him Frisky?
    Ⓓ No mistakes

# Test 5: Language Mechanics (Form C)

**Directions:** For questions 1–7 darken the circle for the word or group of words that has the correct punctuation.

**Sample A**

Disney World is in _____.
- Ⓐ orlando, Florida
- Ⓑ Orlando, florida
- Ⓒ Orlando, Florida
- Ⓓ Orlando Florida

**Time: 15 minutes**

1. Someday we'll all travel in _____.
   - Ⓐ outer space
   - Ⓑ Outer space
   - Ⓒ Outer Space
   - Ⓓ outer Space

2. We celebrate the birthday of _____ every January.
   - Ⓐ Martin luther King, Jr.
   - Ⓑ martin Luther King. Jr.
   - Ⓒ Martin Luther King, jr.
   - Ⓓ Martin Luther King, Jr.

3. *Charlotte's Web* was written by _____.
   - Ⓐ E.B. White
   - Ⓑ e.b. White
   - Ⓒ E.b. White
   - Ⓓ e.b. white

4. The _____ is a great place to visit.
   - Ⓐ Smithsonian institution
   - Ⓑ smithsonian Institution
   - Ⓒ Smithsonian Institution
   - Ⓓ smithsonian institution

5. The _____ is where U.S. Presidents live.
   - Ⓐ white house
   - Ⓑ White House
   - Ⓒ White house
   - Ⓓ white House

6. On _____ our class will plant a tree.
   - Ⓐ arbor Day
   - Ⓑ Arbor day
   - Ⓒ arbor day
   - Ⓓ Arbor Day

7. Vietnam is a _____.
   - Ⓐ Country in Asia
   - Ⓑ country in Asia
   - Ⓒ country in asia
   - Ⓓ Country in asia

**GO ON ⇨**

# Test 5: Language Mechanics (Form C), page 2

**Directions:** For questions 8–13 darken the circle for the correct punctuation for the underlined part. Darken the circle for *Correct as it is* if no punctuaton mark is needed.

**Sample B**

My father likes to watch <u>basketball football, and tennis</u> on television.

Ⓐ !

Ⓑ ;

Ⓒ ,

Ⓓ Correct as it is

8. Which one is <u>Jans sweater?</u>

Ⓐ '

Ⓑ .

Ⓒ ;

Ⓓ Correct as it is

9. "Don't forget to brush your <u>teeth, my mother</u> called.

Ⓐ !

Ⓑ ;

Ⓒ "

Ⓓ Correct as it is

10. Have you ever visited <u>Boston Massachusetts?</u>

Ⓐ ,

Ⓑ :

Ⓒ .

Ⓓ Correct as it is

11. <u>"Sit" I said</u> to my dog.

Ⓐ ?

Ⓑ ;

Ⓒ !

Ⓓ Correct as it is

12. Mr. <u>Locata, our math teacher,</u> taught us how to check our subtraction.

Ⓐ !

Ⓑ ?

Ⓒ ,

Ⓓ Correct as it is

13. Have you ever visited Niagara Falls near <u>Buffalo New York?</u>

Ⓐ ,

Ⓑ ;

Ⓒ .

Ⓓ Correct as it is

# Test 5: Language Mechanics (Form D)

**Directions:** For questions 1–7 darken the circle for the line that has a capitalization mistake. Darken the circle for *No mistakes* if the sentence is correct.

**Sample A**
Ⓐ My sister Ellie is learning
Ⓑ to ice-skate. she practices
Ⓒ for two hours each week.
Ⓓ No mistakes

**Time: 15 minutes**

1. Ⓐ Rose has a new pet.
   Ⓑ It is a canary. She
   Ⓒ named it tweetie.
   Ⓓ No mistakes

2. Ⓐ It was so hot
   Ⓑ last july that we
   Ⓒ couldn't wait for summer
      to end.
   Ⓓ No mistakes

3. Ⓐ We celebrate thanksgiving
   Ⓑ every November. It is
   Ⓒ my favorite holiday.
   Ⓓ No mistakes

4. Ⓐ Stella and i will
   Ⓑ be going to our
   Ⓒ team meeting after school.
   Ⓓ No mistakes

5. Ⓐ My best friend's grandparents
   Ⓑ raise horses on their ranch
   Ⓒ in south Dakota.
   Ⓓ No mistakes

6. Ⓐ Ramon has seen
   Ⓑ all of the *Star Wars*
   Ⓒ movies at least two times.
   Ⓓ No mistakes

7. Ⓐ My mother asked, "who
   Ⓑ wants to go downtown
   Ⓒ with me this afternoon?"
   Ⓓ No mistakes

**GO ON ⇨**

# Test 5: Language Mechanics (Form D), page 2

**Directions:** For questions 8–14 darken the circle for the word or group of words that has the correct punctuation.

**Sample B**

Which is the correct abbreviation for the word *avenue*?

Ⓐ ave,

Ⓑ ave;

Ⓒ ave.

Ⓓ ave,

8. "_____ I would like to have water to drink."

Ⓐ Yes

Ⓑ Yes,

Ⓒ Yes!

Ⓓ Yes;

9. That's a very dangerous

_____

Ⓐ trick!

Ⓑ trick,

Ⓒ trick:

Ⓓ trick?

10. Which is the correct way to end a letter?

Ⓐ Yours truly!

Ⓑ Yours, truly

Ⓒ Yours truly,

Ⓓ Yours truly.

11. My brother was born on

_____.

Ⓐ June, 30 1990

Ⓑ June 30, 1990

Ⓒ June 30 1990

Ⓓ June, 30, 1990

12. Hollywood is in _____.

Ⓐ Los Angeles, California

Ⓑ Los, Angeles, California

Ⓒ Los Angeles: California

Ⓓ Los Angeles; California

13. My _____ friend has a beautiful voice.

Ⓐ mothers

Ⓑ mothers'

Ⓒ mother's

Ⓓ mothe'rs

14. What time will the plane _____

Ⓐ land

Ⓑ land?

Ⓒ land.

Ⓓ land!

**STOP**

# Test 6: Language Expression (Form A)

**Directions:** For questions 1–8 darken the circle for the word that can be used in place of the underlined word or words.

**Sample A**

<u>Ms. Velez</u> will visit us this afternoon.

- (A) They
- (B) Her
- (C) She
- (D) He

**Time: 25 minutes**

1. Jemma wrote a letter to <u>Maida.</u>
   - (A) she
   - (B) her
   - (C) they
   - (D) he

2. This morning <u>Kevin</u> hit a home run.
   - (A) them
   - (B) him
   - (C) we
   - (D) he

3. <u>Robin and Kyle</u> are members of the swim team.
   - (A) They
   - (B) Our
   - (C) Them
   - (D) Their

4. Tanya invited <u>Lola and me</u> to her piano recital.
   - (A) our
   - (B) they
   - (C) we're
   - (D) us

5. <u>Randy and I are</u> reading the same book.
   - (A) They're
   - (B) We're
   - (C) We've
   - (D) Him

6. Tomorrow <u>Renee</u> will get a new bike.
   - (A) her
   - (B) we
   - (C) she
   - (D) us

7. <u>The puppy</u> is very furry.
   - (A) It
   - (B) We
   - (C) They
   - (D) Us

8. <u>The principal</u> gave Jim an award for good work.
   - (A) Our
   - (B) He
   - (C) They
   - (D) We

**GO ON ⇨**

# Test 6: Language Expression (Form A), page 2

**Directions:** For questions 9–14 darken the circle for the word or words that best complete each sentence.

**Sample B**

We like to _____ home from school.

- Ⓐ walked
- Ⓑ walking
- Ⓒ walks
- Ⓓ walk

9. Mr. Scott _____ the school band next year.
- Ⓐ will leading
- Ⓑ will lead
- Ⓒ has leaded
- Ⓓ did lead

10. My best friend _____ coming home with me.
- Ⓐ is
- Ⓑ are
- Ⓒ will
- Ⓓ can't

11. The water dripped _____ into the bowl.
- Ⓐ slow
- Ⓑ slowing
- Ⓒ slowly
- Ⓓ slower

12. Stan is the _____ boy in our class.
- Ⓐ taller
- Ⓑ tallest
- Ⓒ shorted
- Ⓓ shorter

13. When did your dog _____ away?
- Ⓐ running
- Ⓑ runned
- Ⓒ run
- Ⓓ runs

14. Ricky feels _____ today than he felt yesterday.
- Ⓐ bestest
- Ⓑ better
- Ⓒ bested
- Ⓓ best

**GO ON ⇨**

# Test 6: Language Expression (Form A), page 3

**Directions:** For questions 15–19 read the sentence. Then darken the circle for the correct form of the question made from the sentence.

## Sample C
Janet is singing in the chorus.
- Ⓐ In the chorus is Janet singing?
- Ⓑ Singing in the chorus is Janet?
- Ⓒ Is Janet singing in the chorus?
- Ⓓ Janet in the chorus is she singing?

15. Mom will read a story to us later.
- Ⓐ Will Mom read a story to us later?
- Ⓑ Mom a story will read to us later?
- Ⓒ Later a story to us Mom will read?
- Ⓓ A story later Mom will read to us?

16. All dogs can bark.
- Ⓐ Can bark all dogs?
- Ⓑ Bark can all dogs?
- Ⓒ Can all dogs bark?
- Ⓓ Dogs all can bark?

17. It is too early to go.
- Ⓐ Too early is it to go?
- Ⓑ Is it too early to go?
- Ⓒ To go is it too early?
- Ⓓ Too early to go is it?

18. You can help us unpack these games.
- Ⓐ Can you help us unpack these games?
- Ⓑ These games can you help us unpack?
- Ⓒ Unpack these games can you help us?
- Ⓓ These games unpack can you help us?

19. My aunt went to the mall.
- Ⓐ Went to the mall did my aunt?
- Ⓑ To the mall went my aunt?
- Ⓒ Did my aunt go to the mall?
- Ⓓ My aunt did go to the mall?

 **GO ON ⇨**

# Test 6: Language Expression (Form A), page 4

---

**Directions:** For questions 20–23 read the story. Then darken the circle for the sentence that best completes the story.

**Sample D**

Benjamin Franklin believed that lightning was the same thing as electricity. _____. He flew a kite in a storm to get electricity from the lightning.

Ⓐ The kite had a long tail.

Ⓑ Most people didn't believe him.

Ⓒ There was a lot of thunder.

Ⓓ Benjamin Franklin was a printer.

---

20. James Watt tried to find out how to make use of steam. He wanted to use steam to make machinery go. _____.

    Ⓐ The steam engine was a silly idea.

    Ⓑ The steam was very hot.

    Ⓒ The machinery got stuck.

    Ⓓ Finally, he succeeded.

21. Moose are very large animals. An adult moose can weigh almost 2,000 pounds. _____.

    Ⓐ Moose make good pets.

    Ⓑ Male moose have enormous antlers.

    Ⓒ I have never seen a real moose.

    Ⓓ My uncle took a picture of a moose.

22. Tara and her mother took the quilt they made to the county fair. _____. Their quilt won first prize.

    Ⓐ The quilt was torn.

    Ⓑ Tara loved the rides at the fair.

    Ⓒ Tara's father wanted to see the horses.

    Ⓓ They entered the quilt in the quilting contest.

23. Some trees lose their leaves in the fall. Some trees stay green all year. _____.

    Ⓐ They are called evergreens.

    Ⓑ The leaves turn many colors.

    Ⓒ Fall is my favorite time of year.

    Ⓓ We go apple-picking in the fall.

# Test 6: Language Expression (Form B)

**Directions:** For questions 1–7 darken the circle for the word or words that best complete each sentence.

**Sample A**

My sister is _____ than I am.

Ⓐ oldest
Ⓑ more old
Ⓒ older
Ⓓ old

**Time: 25 minutes**

1. If you want to read those books, you can get _____ at the library.
   Ⓐ it
   Ⓑ them
   Ⓒ these
   Ⓓ one

2. We _____ a car coming down the road.
   Ⓐ heard
   Ⓑ hearing
   Ⓒ did heard
   Ⓓ are hear

3. The gray squirrel _____ up and down the tree.
   Ⓐ runned
   Ⓑ run
   Ⓒ ran
   Ⓓ running

4. The third-grade children _____ a party.
   Ⓐ haved
   Ⓑ had
   Ⓒ did having
   Ⓓ did had

5. On their way to the park, they _____ Max.
   Ⓐ seen
   Ⓑ have saw
   Ⓒ had saw
   Ⓓ saw

6. Harry is the _____ boy I know.
   Ⓐ happiest
   Ⓑ happy
   Ⓒ most happiest
   Ⓓ happier

7. Justin _____ the drums in the band.
   Ⓐ did played
   Ⓑ playing
   Ⓒ have played
   Ⓓ played

**GO ON ⇒**

# Test 6: Language Expression (Form B), page 2

**Directions:** For questions 8–13 darken the circle for the sentence that is written correctly.

**Sample B**

Ⓐ The leader the players tell when to begin.

Ⓑ The leader tells the players to.

Ⓒ The leader he tells the players when to begin.

Ⓓ The leader tells the players when to begin.

8. Ⓐ When the wind it blew, the apples.

Ⓑ The wind it blew, the apples down.

Ⓒ When the wind blew, the apples fell.

Ⓓ The apples they fell when the wind blew.

9. Ⓐ The ship docked on Monday morning.

Ⓑ On Monday morning the ship.

Ⓒ On Monday morning the ship it docked.

Ⓓ When the ship docked.

10. Ⓐ Some elephants live.

Ⓑ A very long time is how elephants live.

Ⓒ Some elephants live a very long time.

Ⓓ Some elephants they live a very long time.

11. Ⓐ In the spring the grass it is green.

Ⓑ The grass in the spring.

Ⓒ In the spring the grass is green.

Ⓓ Green is the grass in the spring.

12. Ⓐ It was time to go home for the children.

Ⓑ To go home for the children it was time.

Ⓒ For the children to go home it was time.

Ⓓ It was time for the children to go home.

13. Ⓐ In the bush a nest had a brown bird.

Ⓑ A brown bird had a nest in the bush.

Ⓒ A nest in a bush had a brown bird.

Ⓓ In the bush had a brown bird a nest.

**GO ON ⇨**

# Test 6: Language Expression (Form B), page 3

> **Directions:** For questions 14–20 study the underlined words. Then darken the circle for the simple subject of each sentence.
>
> **Sample C**
> Five girls practiced dancing after school.
> Ⓐ   Ⓑ     Ⓒ           Ⓓ

14. Ruth handed me the blue paper.
    Ⓐ   Ⓑ         Ⓒ   Ⓓ

15. The beautiful spring flowers are in the vase.
        Ⓐ       Ⓑ     Ⓒ           Ⓓ

16. She came in first in the race.
    Ⓐ   Ⓑ     Ⓒ       Ⓓ

17. Her mother is a computer expert.
    Ⓐ   Ⓑ         Ⓒ     Ⓓ

18. Our new television has a large screen.
    Ⓐ   Ⓑ     Ⓒ           Ⓓ

19. We need more construction paper.
    Ⓐ   Ⓑ         Ⓒ     Ⓓ

20. When will the bus leave the station?
        Ⓐ         Ⓑ   Ⓒ       Ⓓ

**GO ON ⇨**

# Test 6: Language Expression (Form B), page 4

---

**Directions:** For questions 21–26 study the underlined words in each sentence. Then darken the circle for the simple predicate of each sentence.

**Sample D**

We <u>baked</u> <u>chocolate</u> chip <u>cookies</u> <u>for</u> the party.
   Ⓐ     Ⓑ        Ⓒ   Ⓓ

---

21. Their <u>new</u> <u>telephone</u> <u>cost</u> more than the <u>old</u> one.
    Ⓐ     Ⓑ    Ⓒ        Ⓓ

22. <u>Denise</u> <u>rushed</u> to the <u>bus</u> <u>stop</u>.
    Ⓐ     Ⓑ      Ⓒ  Ⓓ

23. Eduardo <u>knew</u> the <u>answer</u> to <u>all</u> the <u>riddles</u>.
        Ⓐ      Ⓑ   Ⓒ   Ⓓ

24. The <u>delicious</u> <u>cake</u> <u>really</u> <u>pleased</u> my father.
    Ⓐ   Ⓑ   Ⓒ   Ⓓ

25. <u>Everyone</u> <u>dressed</u> in <u>colorful</u> <u>costumes</u>.
   Ⓐ     Ⓑ     Ⓒ    Ⓓ

26. The <u>giant</u> <u>plane</u> <u>landed</u> on the <u>runway</u>.
    Ⓐ   Ⓑ   Ⓒ      Ⓓ

# Test 6: Language Expression (Form C)

**Directions:** For questions 1–7 darken the circle for the line that has an error in the way the words are used. Darken the circle for *No mistakes* if there is no error.

**Sample A**
- Ⓐ My sister Tiffany she always
- Ⓑ likes to play
- Ⓒ with her dolls.
- Ⓓ No mistakes

**Time: 25 minutes**

1. Ⓐ Because there was a traffic jam,
   - Ⓑ our bus was more than
   - Ⓒ a hour late getting us to school.
   - Ⓓ No mistakes

2. Ⓐ Gary broke a string on his tennis racket.
   - Ⓑ If he can't get it fixed,
   - Ⓒ he won't be able to play in the tournament.
   - Ⓓ No mistakes

3. Ⓐ Larry wanted to eat at
   - Ⓑ MacDiner, but his mother
   - Ⓒ wouldn't give him no money.
   - Ⓓ No mistakes

4. Ⓐ Leslie is learning how to
   - Ⓑ paint with watercolors. She has never
   - Ⓒ use watercolors before.
   - Ⓓ No mistakes

5. Ⓐ Throw them broken cups
   - Ⓑ into the trash bin before
   - Ⓒ someone gets hurt.
   - Ⓓ No mistakes

6. Ⓐ Jeanie did wrote
   - Ⓑ a letter to her
   - Ⓒ grandma and grandpa.
   - Ⓓ No mistakes

7. Ⓐ Sal didn't want
   - Ⓑ nobody to know where
   - Ⓒ he was going after school.
   - Ⓓ No mistakes

GO ON ⇨

Test Practice 3, SV 3787-9

# Test 6: Language Expression (Form C), page 2

**Directions:** For questions 8–14 read each sentence. Then darken the circle for the word or words that will correct the underlined word in the sentence. Darken the circle for *No change* if there is no error.

**Sample B**

When Aunt Polly visits, she <u>will bring</u> us presents.

- Ⓐ bringed
- Ⓑ will bringing
- Ⓒ will brings
- Ⓓ No change

8. I wrapped presents <u>if</u> my mother baked cookies.
- Ⓐ to
- Ⓑ then
- Ⓒ while
- Ⓓ No change

9. After we <u>will walk</u> to town, we were tired.
- Ⓐ walked
- Ⓑ walk
- Ⓒ were walk
- Ⓓ No change

10. Ellie was born <u>in</u> September 18, 1988.
- Ⓐ over
- Ⓑ against
- Ⓒ on
- Ⓓ at

11. Leon <u>goes</u> to camp last summer.
- Ⓐ has gone
- Ⓑ will go
- Ⓒ went
- Ⓓ No change

12. Sylvia leaned <u>against</u> the wall.
- Ⓐ above
- Ⓑ under
- Ⓒ about
- Ⓓ No change

13. I <u>am</u> happy to meet you last week.
- Ⓐ was
- Ⓑ are
- Ⓒ have been
- Ⓓ No change

14. The dog barks <u>wherever</u> he hears the bell ring.
- Ⓐ however
- Ⓑ whenever
- Ⓒ although
- Ⓓ No change

**GO ON ⇨**

# Test 6: Language Expression (Form C), page 3

**Directions:** For questions 15–17 read each pair of sentences. Then darken the circle for the sentence that best combines the two sentences.

## Sample C

Elaine went to the store.
Reggie went to the store, too.

(A) Elaine and Reggie went to the store.

(B) Elaine went to the store, and Reggie went to the store.

(C) To the store went Elaine and Reggie, too.

(D) Elaine went to the store and too went Reggie.

15. My puppy was hiding.
He was hiding under the bench.

(A) My puppy under the bench was hiding.

(B) Under the bench was my puppy hiding.

(C) My puppy he was hiding under the bench.

(D) My puppy was hiding under the bench.

16. Ramona is my best friend.
Ramona is coming to my house.

(A) Ramona to my house is coming my best friend.

(B) My best friend, Ramona, to my house is coming.

(C) My best friend, Ramona, is coming to my house.

(D) Ramona, my best friend, she is coming to my house.

17. The package is in my closet.
It is on the top shelf.

(A) On the top shelf is the package in my closet.

(B) The package is on the top shelf in my closet.

(C) The package on the top shelf is in my closet.

(D) In my closet is the package on the top shelf.

**GO ON ⇨**

# Test 6: Language Expression (Form C), page 4

**Directions:** For questions 18–20 read each paragraph. Then darken the circle for the correct answer.

The house was beside a railroad track. It was a lonely place, with no other houses or stores in sight. Maurice's father was keeper of the gates that shut off the road when a train came through.

**18.** Which is the best opening sentence for this paragraph?
- Ⓐ Maurice watched the trains go by that day.
- Ⓑ Maurice lived in a small stone house in the country.
- Ⓒ There was a boy named Maurice.
- Ⓓ Maurice liked trains.

**1.** One day late in August, Joey heard a strange roaring sound. **2.** The birds turned in a big circle and settled down in a cornfield. **3.** It was made by the wings of blackbirds as they flew overhead. **4.** Then they flew away. **5.** Joey had never seen so many birds at one time.

**19.** Where does sentence 3 belong?
- Ⓐ where it is now
- Ⓑ between sentences 4 and 5
- Ⓒ after sentence 2
- Ⓓ after sentence 1

**1.** The bear's paw struck the water hard. **2.** It threw something silvery on the ground. **3.** It was a fish. **4.** Fish are good for you. **5.** The bear had caught it with its big, hairy paw. **6.** The bear kept its eye on the water.

**20.** Which sentence does not belong in this paragraph?
- Ⓐ Sentence 3
- Ⓑ Sentence 4
- Ⓒ Sentence 1
- Ⓓ Sentence 5

# Test 6: Language Expression (Form D)

**Directions:** For questions 1–4 read each paragraph. Then darken the circle for the correct answer.

**Time: 25 minutes**

1. Which is a good opening sentence for this paragraph?
   _____. It is the largest island in the world. It is nearly three times the size of the second largest island.
   - Ⓐ There are many large islands.
   - Ⓑ Greenland is a huge island.
   - Ⓒ Greenland is a cold island.
   - Ⓓ The ice stays frozen all year long.

2. Which is a good closing sentence for this paragraph?
   Some people are concerned about the amount of water we are using. They are worried about the water supply for the future. _____.
   - Ⓐ Water is important for everyone.
   - Ⓑ Farmers need water for their plants.
   - Ⓒ They say that everyone must conserve water.
   - Ⓓ Water is stored in reservoirs.

3. Which is a good opening sentence for this paragraph?
   _____. When it ripened, the Pilgrims harvested it. Then the Indians taught the Pilgrims how to use the corn for food.
   - Ⓐ The Pilgrims were good farmers.
   - Ⓑ The Indians taught the Pilgrims how to plant corn.
   - Ⓒ The Pilgrims wanted to have good crops.
   - Ⓓ Corn is a useful crop.

4. Which is a good closing sentence for this paragraph?
   Some of the soldiers in the Revolutionary War were called "Minutemen." They were given this name because they had to be prepared to fight. Minutemen had to be ready at a minute's notice. _____.
   - Ⓐ Minutemen helped to win the Revolutionary War.
   - Ⓑ Everyone thought it was a silly name.
   - Ⓒ Minutemen didn't have any training.
   - Ⓓ Minutemen were pretty good fighters.

**GO ON ⇨**

Name _____ Date _____

# Test 6: Language Expression (Form D), page 2

**Directions:** For questions 5–7 read the sentence. Darken the circle for the word or words that fit the sentence.

**Sample A**

Marci _____ in the school office.
- Ⓐ working
- Ⓑ did work
- Ⓒ had working
- Ⓓ works

5. The children _____ turns going down the slide.
   - Ⓐ took
   - Ⓑ taken
   - Ⓒ have took
   - Ⓓ taked

6. Chelsea _____ the scraps of paper in the basket.
   - Ⓐ throwed
   - Ⓑ has threw
   - Ⓒ had throwing
   - Ⓓ threw

7. Shawn _____ his fish every day.
   - Ⓐ has feeded
   - Ⓑ fed
   - Ⓒ did feed
   - Ⓓ have fed

**Directions:** For questions 8–10 darken the circle for the pronoun that can replace the underlined word or words.

**Sample B**

Did <u>Rhea</u> finish her homework?
- Ⓐ it
- Ⓑ she
- Ⓒ they
- Ⓓ he

8. <u>Debbi and Jamie</u> are setting the table.
   - Ⓐ They
   - Ⓑ Them
   - Ⓒ We
   - Ⓓ Their

9. <u>You and I</u> have to go shopping later.
   - Ⓐ Us
   - Ⓑ Our
   - Ⓒ We
   - Ⓓ She

10. Please give <u>Sandy and me</u> the homework assignment.
    - Ⓐ I
    - Ⓑ us
    - Ⓒ we
    - Ⓓ they

**GO ON ⇨**

Test Practice 3, SV 3787-9

# Test 6: Language Expression (Form D), page 3

---

**Directions:** For questions 11–13 study the underlined words. Then darken the circle for the simple subject.

**Sample C**

The <u>cup</u> had a <u>broken</u> <u>handle</u>.
Ⓐ Ⓑ      Ⓒ    Ⓓ

---

11. <u>Ms. Ramos</u> put the <u>birthday</u> <u>cards</u> on her <u>desk</u>.
    Ⓐ                Ⓑ    Ⓒ      Ⓓ

12. This <u>summer</u> the <u>boys</u> will <u>go</u> to <u>camp</u>.
       Ⓐ        Ⓑ     Ⓒ    Ⓓ

13. <u>Norman's</u> <u>letter</u> was <u>sent</u> to the wrong <u>address</u>.
    Ⓐ     Ⓑ      Ⓒ           Ⓓ

---

**Directions:** For questions 14–16 study the underlined words. Then darken the circle for the simple predicate.

**Sample D**

Her new <u>shoes</u> <u>shine</u> <u>very</u> <u>brightly</u>.
      Ⓐ     Ⓑ     Ⓒ    Ⓓ

---

14. The <u>music</u> class <u>began</u> at <u>five</u> <u>o'clock</u>.
       Ⓐ        Ⓑ     Ⓒ   Ⓓ

15. <u>Charlie</u> <u>quickly</u> <u>answered</u> the <u>question</u>.
    Ⓐ      Ⓑ      Ⓒ      Ⓓ

16. <u>Our</u> class <u>read</u> about <u>the Civil War</u>.
    Ⓐ      Ⓑ      Ⓒ   Ⓓ

**GO ON ⇨**

# Test 6: Language Expression (Form D), page 4

**Directions:** For questions 17–21 darken the circle for the sentence that is written most clearly.

**Sample E**

(A) Many fields of wheat in the country were.

(B) Many fields of wheat were.

(C) Many fields of were wheat in the country.

(D) In the country were many fields of wheat.

17. (A) The enemy they escaped from.

(B) They escaped from the enemy.

(C) They from the enemy escaped.

(D) Escaped from the enemy they.

18. (A) Patti tied a string around her finger.

(B) Around her finger did Patti tie a string.

(C) Patti did tie a string.

(D) A string Patti tied around her finger.

19. (A) Yesterday in the yard were the children playing.

(B) In the yard were the children playing yesterday.

(C) The children in the yard.

(D) The children were playing in the yard yesterday.

20. (A) A thick bushy tail.

(B) The squirrel has a thick bushy tail.

(C) A thick bushy tail has the squirrel.

(D) The squirrel a thick bushy tail has.

21. (A) When they heard a noise did they stop.

(B) They stopped when they heard a noise.

(C) A noise they heard so when they stopped.

(D) They heard a noise stopped did they.

# Test 7: Mathematics Computation (Form A)

**Directions:** For questions 1–4 darken the circle for the correct answer to the addition problems. For questions 5–7 darken the circle for the correct answer to the subtraction problems. If the correct answer is not given, darken the circle for *None of these*.

**Time: 15 minutes**

1.  1,283
    + 1,506

    Ⓐ 2,789
    Ⓑ 3,789
    Ⓒ 2,709
    Ⓓ None of these

2. $463 + 27 =$
    Ⓐ 480
    Ⓑ 580
    Ⓒ 490
    Ⓓ None of these

3. $52 + 10 + 5 =$
    Ⓐ 77
    Ⓑ 67
    Ⓒ 62
    Ⓓ None of these

4.  $0.12
    + 0.79

    Ⓐ $0.91
    Ⓑ $0.81
    Ⓒ $0.87
    Ⓓ None of these

5. $47 - 15 =$
    Ⓐ 31
    Ⓑ 32
    Ⓒ 25
    Ⓓ None of these

6.  60
    − 3

    Ⓐ 50
    Ⓑ 40
    Ⓒ 57
    Ⓓ None of these

7. $$6.64 - $0.42 =$
    Ⓐ $6.40
    Ⓑ $5.42
    Ⓒ $6.22
    Ⓓ None of these

**GO ON ⇨**

# Test 7: Mathematics Computation (Form A),
## page 2

**Directions:** For questions 8–11 darken the circle for the correct answer to the multiplication problems. For questions 12–15 darken the circle for the correct answer to the division problems. If the correct answer is not given, darken the circle for *None of these.*

**8.**
$$\begin{array}{r} 7 \\ \times 5 \\ \hline \end{array}$$

- Ⓐ 12
- Ⓑ 30
- Ⓒ 28
- Ⓓ None of these

**9.** $3 \times 312 =$
- Ⓐ 636
- Ⓑ 936
- Ⓒ 946
- Ⓓ None of these

**10.**
$$\begin{array}{r} 52 \\ \times \ 2 \\ \hline \end{array}$$

- Ⓐ 104
- Ⓑ 74
- Ⓒ 94
- Ⓓ None of these

**11.** $6 \times 10 =$
- Ⓐ 0
- Ⓑ 16
- Ⓒ 60
- Ⓓ None of these

**12.** $8 \div 7 =$
- Ⓐ 1 R1
- Ⓑ 1
- Ⓒ 1 R7
- Ⓓ None of these

**13.** $35 \div 7 =$
- Ⓐ 5 R2
- Ⓑ 5 R1
- Ⓒ 7
- Ⓓ None of these

**14.** $6\overline{)0}$
- Ⓐ 60
- Ⓑ 0
- Ⓒ 1
- Ⓓ None of these

**15.** $3\overline{)27}$
- Ⓐ 9
- Ⓑ 7
- Ⓒ 8
- Ⓓ None of these

STOP

Test Practice 3, SV 3787-9

# Test 7: Mathematics Computation (Form B)

**Directions:** For questions 1–6 darken the circle for the correct answer. Darken the circle for *Not given* if the correct answer is *not* given.

**Sample A**

**Add:** 8
     + 6

Ⓐ 16
Ⓑ 18
Ⓒ 14
Ⓓ Not given

**Time: 15 minutes**

**1.** 7 + 3 + 5 =
    Ⓐ 15
    Ⓑ 14
    Ⓒ 12
    Ⓓ Not given

**2.**    42
         52
       + 20

    Ⓐ  94
    Ⓑ 104
    Ⓒ 114
    Ⓓ Not given

**3.**    400
        + 200

    Ⓐ    6
    Ⓑ   60
    Ⓒ  600
    Ⓓ Not given

**4.**  $0.44
       + 0.73

    Ⓐ $1.27
    Ⓑ $1.17
    Ⓒ $1.07
    Ⓓ Not given

**5.** 423 + 18 =
    Ⓐ 431
    Ⓑ 421
    Ⓒ 541
    Ⓓ Not given

**6.** 12 + 3 + 5 =
    Ⓐ 19
    Ⓑ 20
    Ⓒ 21
    Ⓓ Not given

**GO ON ⇨**

Name _____ Date _____

# Test 7: Mathematics Computation (Form B),
## page 2

**Directions:** For questions 7–13 darken the circle for the correct answer. Darken the circle for *Not given* if the correct answer is not given.

**Sample B**
**Subtract:** $42 - 5 =$
- Ⓐ 47
- Ⓑ 27
- Ⓒ 37
- Ⓓ Not given

7.  $$625 \\ -\ 25$$
- Ⓐ 620
- Ⓑ 605
- Ⓒ 650
- Ⓓ Not given

8.  $$470 \\ -\ 80$$
- Ⓐ 390
- Ⓑ 480
- Ⓒ 410
- Ⓓ Not given

9. $90 - 70 =$
- Ⓐ 30
- Ⓑ 10
- Ⓒ 20
- Ⓓ Not given

10. $73 - 14 =$
- Ⓐ 67
- Ⓑ 59
- Ⓒ 69
- Ⓓ Not given

11.  $$204 \\ -\ 12$$
- Ⓐ 102
- Ⓑ 92
- Ⓒ 192
- Ⓓ Not given

12. $15 - 8 =$
- Ⓐ 9
- Ⓑ 7
- Ⓒ 8
- Ⓓ Not given

13. $78 - 9 =$
- Ⓐ 69
- Ⓑ 68
- Ⓒ 67
- Ⓓ Not given

**STOP**

# Test 7: Mathematics Computation (Form C)

**Directions:** For questions 1–4 darken the circle for the correct answer to the addition problems. For questions 5–7 darken the circle for the correct answer to the subtraction problems. Darken the circle for *Not given* if the correct answer is *not* given.

**Time: 15 minutes**

1. $711 + 2 + 64 =$
   Ⓐ 777
   Ⓑ 707
   Ⓒ 727
   Ⓓ Not given

2. 
   $$\begin{array}{r} 17 \\ 36 \\ +\ 5 \\ \hline \end{array}$$
   Ⓐ 48
   Ⓑ 57
   Ⓒ 58
   Ⓓ Not given

3. $32 + 31 =$
   Ⓐ 63
   Ⓑ 62
   Ⓒ 73
   Ⓓ Not given

4. 
   $$\begin{array}{r} \$2.05 \\ +\ 1.15 \\ \hline \end{array}$$
   Ⓐ $3.10
   Ⓑ $3.20
   Ⓒ $3.15
   Ⓓ Not given

5. $854 - 3 =$
   Ⓐ 801
   Ⓑ 857
   Ⓒ 851
   Ⓓ Not given

6. 
   $$\begin{array}{r} 107 \\ -\ 26 \\ \hline \end{array}$$
   Ⓐ 101
   Ⓑ 17
   Ⓒ 81
   Ⓓ Not given

7. 
   $$\begin{array}{r} \$0.96 \\ -\ 0.37 \\ \hline \end{array}$$
   Ⓐ $0.61
   Ⓑ $0.69
   Ⓒ $0.59
   Ⓓ Not given

**GO ON ⇨**

Name _____  Date _____

# Test 7: Mathematics Computation (Form C),
## page 2

**Directions:** For questions 8–11 darken the circle for the correct answer to the multiplication problems. For questions 12–15 darken the circle for the correct answer to the division problems. Darken the circle for *Not given* if the answer is *not* given.

8. $502 \times 3 =$
   - Ⓐ 1,506
   - Ⓑ 1,560
   - Ⓒ 1,660
   - Ⓓ Not given

9. $\begin{array}{r} 35 \\ \times\ 3 \\ \hline \end{array}$
   - Ⓐ 150
   - Ⓑ 305
   - Ⓒ 105
   - Ⓓ Not given

10. $2 \times 322 =$
   - Ⓐ 644
   - Ⓑ 744
   - Ⓒ 544
   - Ⓓ Not given

11. $\begin{array}{r} 36 \\ \times\ 7 \\ \hline \end{array}$
   - Ⓐ 213
   - Ⓑ 252
   - Ⓒ 313
   - Ⓓ Not given

12. $6 \div 3 =$
   - Ⓐ 3
   - Ⓑ 2
   - Ⓒ 9
   - Ⓓ Not given

13. $7\overline{)210}$
   - Ⓐ 3
   - Ⓑ 30
   - Ⓒ 5
   - Ⓓ Not given

14. $45 \div 9 =$
   - Ⓐ 5
   - Ⓑ 6
   - Ⓒ 7
   - Ⓓ Not given

15. $6 \div 0 =$
   - Ⓐ 1
   - Ⓑ 60
   - Ⓒ 10
   - Ⓓ Not given

**STOP**

# Test 7: Mathematics Computation (Form D)

**Directions:** For questions 1–6 darken the circle for the correct answer. Darken the circle for *Not given* if the correct answer is *not* given.

## Sample A

37
+ 3

Ⓐ 30
Ⓑ 34
Ⓒ 40
Ⓓ Not given

**Time: 15 minutes**

**1.**   611
18
+ 73

Ⓐ 712
Ⓑ 702
Ⓒ 722
Ⓓ Not given

**2.** $5 \times 8 =$
Ⓐ 40
Ⓑ 35
Ⓒ 45
Ⓓ Not given

**3.**   234
− 128

Ⓐ 122
Ⓑ 112
Ⓒ 106
Ⓓ Not given

**4.** $8 \div 2 =$
Ⓐ 3
Ⓑ 4
Ⓒ 6
Ⓓ Not given

**5.**   7
× 7

Ⓐ 49
Ⓑ 14
Ⓒ 24
Ⓓ Not given

**6.** $5 \times 407 =$
Ⓐ 2,350
Ⓑ 2,305
Ⓒ 2,035

**GO ON ⇨**

# Test 7: Mathematics Computation (Form D),
## page 2

**Directions:** For questions 7–10 darken the circle for the correct answer. Darken the circle for *Not given* if the correct answer is *not* given.

### Sample B

Delia has to put 35 books on the library shelf. She has already put 18 books on the shelf. How many more books does she still have to put on the shelf?

Ⓐ  18
Ⓑ  19
Ⓒ  17
Ⓓ  Not given

7. Leonard's mother cut a pizza pie into six pieces. Two of the pieces have been eaten. How many pieces are left?

Ⓐ  2
Ⓑ  4
Ⓒ  6
Ⓓ  Not given

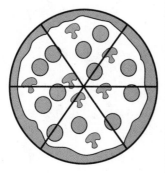

8. Ted's aunt gave him six shells. His friend gave him six more. Ted gave away three that were alike. How many shells did he have left?

Ⓐ  9
Ⓑ  3
Ⓒ  12
Ⓓ  Not given

9. Terri has a new box of felt-tip markers. She has three red markers, four blue markers, and three green markers. How many markers does she have altogether?

Ⓐ  12
Ⓑ  9
Ⓒ  10
Ⓓ  Not given

10. Molly invited nine friends to her house. She wants to give each of them four cookies. How many cookies will she need?

Ⓐ  13
Ⓑ  31
Ⓒ  36
Ⓓ  Not given

Name _____  Date _____

# Test 8: Mathematics Concepts/Applications (Form A)

**Directions:** For questions 1–18 darken the circle for the correct answer.

## Sample A

In which place is zero in the number 2,305?

Ⓐ ones
Ⓑ tens
Ⓒ hundreds
Ⓓ thousands

## Sample B

Kyle saved $5.00 to buy a present for his mother. The present he wants to buy costs $12.00. How much more money does Kyle need?

Ⓐ $17.00
Ⓑ $7.00
Ⓒ $2.00
Ⓓ $10.00

**Time: 22 minutes**

1. Which is the Roman numeral for 39?
   Ⓐ XXXIX
   Ⓑ IIIIX
   Ⓒ XXXX
   Ⓓ IXXXX

2. Mrs. Stellato wants to buy both of these T-shirts. What is the best estimate of how much the shirts will cost?
   Ⓐ $40
   Ⓑ $20
   Ⓒ $30
   Ⓓ $15

3. Which number is missing in this pattern?
   10, 12, ___, 16, 18
   Ⓐ 13
   Ⓑ 14
   Ⓒ 15
   Ⓓ 12

4. Vera leaves home at 9:00 A.M. every day. It takes her 15 minutes to walk to school. Which clock shows the time she gets to school?

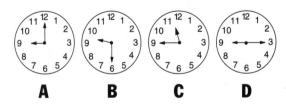

   A        B        C        D

   Ⓐ A
   Ⓑ B
   Ⓒ C
   Ⓓ D

GO ON ⇒

# Test 8: Mathematics Concepts/Applications
## (Form A), page 2

> **Directions:** Use the calendar to answer questions 5 and 6.

### November

| Sun | Mon | Tues | Wed | Thur | Fri | Sat |
|-----|-----|------|-----|------|-----|-----|
|     |     |      | 1   | 2    | 3   | 4   |
| 5   | 6   | 7    | 8   | 9    | 10  | 11  |
| 12  | 13  | 14   | 15  | 16   | 17  | 18  |
| 19  | 20  | 21   | 22  | 23   | 24  | 25  |
| 26  | 27  | 28   | 29  | 30   |     |     |

**5.** Aviva will have her birthday party on the third Thursday of the month. What is the date of Aviva's party?
- Ⓐ 23
- Ⓑ 9
- Ⓒ 16
- Ⓓ 30

**6.** What day of the week is November 21?
- Ⓐ Sunday
- Ⓑ Friday
- Ⓒ Wednesday
- Ⓓ Tuesday

**7.** Which would you use to measure length?
- Ⓐ ounce
- Ⓑ inch
- Ⓒ pound
- Ⓓ degree

**8.** Which number is the same as three thousand four hundred thirty-five?
- Ⓐ 3,435
- Ⓑ 3,534
- Ⓒ 4,335
- Ⓓ 3,453

**9.** Which symbol belongs in the blank space?

☆ ☆ ○ ○ △ __ ▢ ▢

- Ⓐ star
- Ⓑ square
- Ⓒ triangle
- Ⓓ circle

**10.** Valerie has three coins in her pocket. Which amount could she not have?
- Ⓐ 15 cents
- Ⓑ 40 cents
- Ⓒ 17 cents
- Ⓓ 60 cents

**11.** Which of these figures is all rectangles?
- Ⓐ A
- Ⓑ B
- Ⓒ C
- Ⓓ D

**GO ON ⇨**

# Test 8: Mathematics Concepts/Applications
## (Form A), page 3

**12.** Which is the best estimate of the temperature of a cup of hot chocolate?

- Ⓐ 110° F
- Ⓑ 22° F
- Ⓒ 60° F
- Ⓓ 75° F

**13.** Which of the following would you use to estimate 63 plus 22?

- Ⓐ 70 and 20
- Ⓑ 70 and 30
- Ⓒ 60 and 20
- Ⓓ 60 and 30

**14.** Which number sentence has an answer that is an even number?

- Ⓐ 9 + 2 =
- Ⓑ 7 + 7 =
- Ⓒ 7 + 8 =
- Ⓓ 9 + 4 =

**15.** Which stick is less than 2 inches?

- Ⓐ A
- Ⓑ B
- Ⓒ C
- Ⓓ D

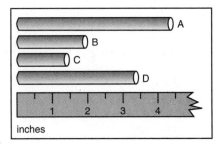

**16.** Which of these groups of numbers has an odd number between two even numbers?

- Ⓐ 26, 30, 42
- Ⓑ 44, 57, 64
- Ⓒ 18, 34, 38
- Ⓓ 62, 76, 84

**17.** Which of these has a star in the open figure?

- Ⓐ A
- Ⓑ B
- Ⓒ C
- Ⓓ D

**18.** This graph shows how much money the children at Northside School made at their puppet show. Which fraction shows how much of the money came from admissions?

- Ⓐ $\frac{1}{3}$
- Ⓑ $\frac{1}{2}$
- Ⓒ $\frac{1}{4}$
- Ⓓ $\frac{2}{3}$

# Test 8: Mathematics Concepts/Applications (Form B)

**Directions:** For questions 1–16 darken the circle for the correct answer.

## Sample A

Which sign should go in the ☐ ?

8 ☐ 7 = 56

Ⓐ +

Ⓑ −

Ⓒ ×

Ⓓ ÷

## Sample B

Jeremy bought a model car kit for $2.98. He gave the clerk $5.00. About how much change will he receive?

Ⓐ $3.00

Ⓑ $1.02

Ⓒ $2.20

Ⓓ $2.00

**Time: 20 minutes**

1. How many hearts should there be in the next square?

Ⓐ 8

Ⓑ 9

Ⓒ 6

Ⓓ 5

**Directions:** The students at the Parkway School earn coupons for helping out in the office and on the playground. They can use the coupons to buy supplies in the school supply store. Use the picture to answer questions 2–5.

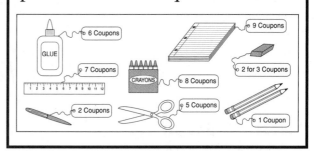

2. Jeremy needs a new ruler but he only has five coupons. Adam said that he will lend Jeremy the coupons he needs. How many coupons will Adam lend to Jeremy?

Ⓐ 9

Ⓑ 5

Ⓒ 2

Ⓓ 7

3. How many coupons does Wanda need to buy crayons, a ruler, and a pair of scissors?

Ⓐ 17

Ⓑ 15

Ⓒ 20

Ⓓ 19

**GO ON ⇨**

# Test 8: Mathematics Concepts/Applications
## (Form B), page 2

4. Saul decided to get erasers for eight of his friends. How many coupons will he need?
   - (A) 12
   - (B) 5
   - (C) 8
   - (D) 14

5. Tessie has 18 coupons. She wants to buy a bottle of glue and a pack of paper. How many coupons will she have left?
   - (A) 3 coupons
   - (B) 4 coupons
   - (C) 2 coupons
   - (D) 0 coupons

6. How many paper clips are shown here?

   - (A) 11 clips
   - (B) 30 clips
   - (C) 37 clips
   - (D) 40 clips

7. Which number tells how many squares there are?

   - (A) 300
   - (B) 239
   - (C) 327
   - (D) 232

8. Eric's mother is making sweaters for Eric and his brother. Each sweater will need six buttons. How many packages of buttons will she have to buy to have enough for both sweaters?
   - (A) 2 packages
   - (B) 4 packages
   - (C) 1 package
   - (D) 3 packages

   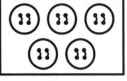

9. Which is the closest estimate of $879 – $410?
   - (A) $900 – $400
   - (B) $800 – $400
   - (C) $800 – $500
   - (D) $700 – $400

**GO ON ⇨**

# Test 8: Mathematics Concepts/Applications
## (Form B), page 3

**10.** According to this chart, what number should go in the Out box next to 5?

| In | Out |
|---|---|
| 7 | 28 |
| 6 |  |
| 5 |  |

x 4

Ⓐ 20
Ⓑ 16
Ⓒ 24
Ⓓ 8

**11.** Delia is going to visit her cousins on June 3. She plans to stay one week. On what day will she return home?

Ⓐ May 30
Ⓑ July 10
Ⓒ June 10
Ⓓ April 10

**12.** Which is another way to write 917?

Ⓐ 900 + 10 + 7
Ⓑ 900 + 7
Ⓒ 90 + 100 + 7
Ⓓ 90 + 10 + 7

**13.** Which piece was cut out of this folded card?

Ⓐ A
Ⓑ B
Ⓒ C
Ⓓ D

B ⬤     C ◇

A ▷     D ▭

**14.** Which number sentence can you use to check the answer to this number sentence?

16 – 9 = 7

Ⓐ 9 + 9 = 18
Ⓑ 16 + 9 = 25
Ⓒ 9 + 7 = 16
Ⓓ 9 – 7 = 2

**Directions:** Use the chart to answer questions 15–16.

| Carnation | 🌷🌷🌷🌷🌷🌷🌷 |
|---|---|
| Lily | 🌼🌼🌼🌼 |
| Daisy | 🌻🌻🌻 |
| Tulip | 🌷🌷 |
| Rose | 🌹🌹🌹🌹🌹🌹 |

**15.** How many more roses than tulips are shown?

Ⓐ 6
Ⓑ 4
Ⓒ 3
Ⓓ 2

**16.** How many fewer daisies than carnations are shown?

Ⓐ 3
Ⓑ 7
Ⓒ 5
Ⓓ 2

STOP

# Test 8 Mathematics Concepts/Applications Form C

**Directions:** For questions 1–19 darken the circle for the correct answer. Darken the circle for *Not given* if the correct answer is *not* given.

## Sample A
Which is the correct way to write 600 + 70 + 3?
- Ⓐ 6,073
- Ⓑ 673
- Ⓒ 6,703
- Ⓓ Not given

## Sample B
Carla collects Beanie Babies. She has 72 different ones. Last week her Aunt Martha bought 4 new Beanie Babies for her. How many does Carla have now?
- Ⓐ 78
- Ⓑ 80
- Ⓒ 76
- Ⓓ Not given

**Time: 25 minutes**

1. How many square units are in this figure?
   - Ⓐ 12
   - Ⓑ 13
   - Ⓒ 11
   - Ⓓ Not given

   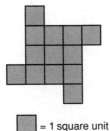

   = 1 square unit

2. Which set of coins is worth the most money?
   - Ⓐ 8 nickels
   - Ⓑ 3 dimes
   - Ⓒ 2 quarters
   - Ⓓ 12 pennies

3. How many stars belong to the circle and the square?
   - Ⓐ 4 stars
   - Ⓑ 6 stars
   - Ⓒ 8 stars
   - Ⓓ 5 stars

4. Look at the sandwich cut into parts. Which fraction shows how much one part of this sandwich equals?
   - Ⓐ $\frac{1}{2}$
   - Ⓑ $\frac{1}{3}$
   - Ⓒ $\frac{1}{4}$
   - Ⓓ Not given

   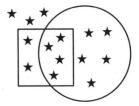

5. Which is the closest estimate of $7 \times 18$?
   - Ⓐ between 50 and 100
   - Ⓑ between 100 and 150
   - Ⓒ between 150 and 200
   - Ⓓ Not given

**GO ON ⇨**

# Test 8: Mathematics Concepts/Applications
## (Form C), page 2

**6.** What numeral makes this number sentence correct?

$9 - 6 + 8 = \square + 5 + 4$

Ⓐ 2
Ⓑ 3
Ⓒ 4
Ⓓ Not given

---

**Directions:** Use the chart to answer questions 7–9.

|  | Kareem | Delia | Ling | Stacy |
|---|---|---|---|---|
| Game 1 | ℍℍ // | // | ℍℍ | / |
| Game 2 | ℍℍ | ℍℍ | ℍℍ | ℍℍ |
| Game 3 | ℍℍ ℍℍ | ℍℍ | / | /// |

---

**7.** Which student had a total of 22 points in all three games?

Ⓐ Kareem
Ⓑ Delia
Ⓒ Stacy
Ⓓ Not given

**8.** Who had the least number of points in game 3?

Ⓐ Stacy
Ⓑ Ling
Ⓒ Kareem
Ⓓ Not given

**9.** Who scored the second highest number of points in game 3?

Ⓐ Ling
Ⓑ Stacy
Ⓒ Delia
Ⓓ Not given

**10.** How many degrees does this thermometer show?

Ⓐ 69
Ⓑ 72
Ⓒ 60
Ⓓ Not given

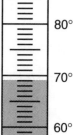

**11.** Which figure is $\frac{3}{4}$ shaded?

Ⓐ A
Ⓑ B
Ⓒ C
Ⓓ D

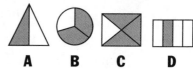

A    B    C    D

**12.** Which is another name for 8 hundreds, 0 tens, and 3 ones?

Ⓐ 830
Ⓑ 803
Ⓒ 83
Ⓓ Not given

**GO ON ⇨**

# Test 8: Mathematics Concepts/Applications
## (Form C), page 3

**13.** How many more pictures can this photo cube hold?

- Ⓐ 6
- Ⓑ 5
- Ⓒ 4
- Ⓓ Not given

**14.** Which figure shows a line of symmetry?

- Ⓐ A
- Ⓑ B
- Ⓒ C
- Ⓓ D

**Directions:** Use this chart to answer questions 15–17.

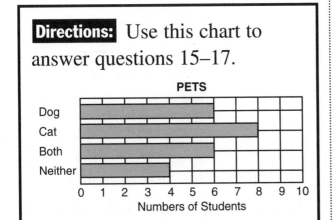

**PETS**

**15.** How many students have dogs?

- Ⓐ 4
- Ⓑ 6
- Ⓒ 3
- Ⓓ Not given

**16.** How many students do not have either pet?

- Ⓐ 4
- Ⓑ 8
- Ⓒ 2
- Ⓓ Not given

**17.** How many students have both cats and dogs?

- Ⓐ 8
- Ⓑ 7
- Ⓒ 6
- Ⓓ Not given

**18.** Which number is closest in value to 600 when rounded?

- Ⓐ 60
- Ⓑ 699
- Ⓒ 602
- Ⓓ 589

**19.** What is the perimeter of this rectangle?

- Ⓐ 100 feet
- Ⓑ 50 feet
- Ⓒ 30 feet
- Ⓓ Not given

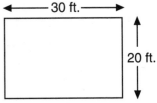

STOP

# Test 8: Mathematics Concepts/Applications (Form D)

**Directions:** For questions 1–18 darken the circle for the correct answer.

## Sample A

Which figure is a square?

Ⓐ A
Ⓑ B
Ⓒ C
Ⓓ D

B
C
A
D

## Sample B

Molly bought a box of candy for $3.59. She paid $0.19 tax. How much did she spend altogether?

Ⓐ $3.80
Ⓑ $3.78
Ⓒ $3.87
Ⓓ $3.72

**Time: 22 minutes**

1. One of the movie theaters in the new cineplex has 763 seats. What is that number rounded to the nearest hundred?

Ⓐ 700
Ⓑ 800
Ⓒ 900
Ⓓ 750

2. Which fraction shows how many banners are white?

Ⓐ $\frac{1}{2}$
Ⓑ $\frac{1}{4}$
Ⓒ $\frac{1}{3}$
Ⓓ $\frac{1}{5}$

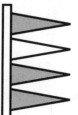

3. How many more large squares are needed to fill this rectangle?

Ⓐ 4
Ⓑ 6
Ⓒ 3
Ⓓ 5

4. Which is another name for 429?

Ⓐ forty two nine
Ⓑ four hundred twenty-nine
Ⓒ four hundred two nine
Ⓓ four hundred two ninety

5. How many spaces on the number line did the frog jump over?

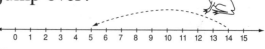

Ⓐ 10
Ⓑ 8
Ⓒ 11
Ⓓ 9

**GO ON ⇨**

# Test 8: Mathematics Concepts/Applications
## (Form D), page 2

**6.** Which is the closest estimate of 329 + 588?
- Ⓐ 900
- Ⓑ 800
- Ⓒ 1,000
- Ⓓ 600

**7.** Which number tells how many blocks are shown here?
- Ⓐ 427
- Ⓑ 327
- Ⓒ 37
- Ⓓ 307

**8.** What is the missing number in this pattern?

70, 65, 60, 55, _____
- Ⓐ 75
- Ⓑ 45
- Ⓒ 80
- Ⓓ 50

**Directions:** Mr. Lyons' third-grade class kept a record of the books they read. Use the chart to answer questions 9–11.

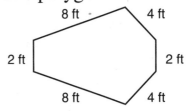

**9.** How many books did Don read?
- Ⓐ 10
- Ⓑ 5
- Ⓒ 8
- Ⓓ 12

**10.** Who read two times as many books as Eloisa and Carrie combined?
- Ⓐ Nick
- Ⓑ Don
- Ⓒ Sue
- Ⓓ Carrie

**11.** How many more books did Don read than Carrie?
- Ⓐ 4
- Ⓑ 8
- Ⓒ 6
- Ⓓ 2

**12.** What is the perimeter of this polygon?

8 ft   4 ft
2 ft   2 ft
8 ft   4 ft

- Ⓐ 28 feet
- Ⓑ 18 feet
- Ⓒ 20 feet
- Ⓓ 10 feet

**GO ON ⇨**

# Test 8: Mathematics Concepts/Applications
## (Form D), page 3

**13.** Which unit is best to use to measure the weight of a crayon?

Ⓐ gram
Ⓑ pound
Ⓒ inch
Ⓓ foot

**14.** Tyrone wants to buy four balloons and a bag of marbles. If he gives the clerk $2.00, how much change will he get back?

Ⓐ $0.90
Ⓑ $0.80
Ⓒ $0.70
Ⓓ $0.75

**15.** Which of these figures is congruent with the top figure?

**A**    **B**    **D**

Ⓐ A
Ⓑ B
Ⓒ C
Ⓓ None of these

**16.** What number is missing in this pattern?

5, 8, 11, ____, 17, 20

Ⓐ 13
Ⓑ 15
Ⓒ 14
Ⓓ 12

**17.** What is the area of this shape in square units?

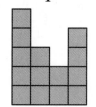

☐ = 1 square unit

Ⓐ 12 square units
Ⓑ 14 square units
Ⓒ 10 square units
Ⓓ 16 square units

**18.** Which is another way to write $6 \times 3$?

Ⓐ $6 \times 6 \times 6$
Ⓑ $3 + 3 + 3 + 3 + 3 + 3$
Ⓒ $18 \div 6$
Ⓓ $3 \times 3 \times 3$

**STOP**

# Test 9: Study Skills (Form A)

**Directions:** For questions 1–14 darken the circle for the correct answer.

For questions 1–7 choose the word or name that would come *first* if the words in each group were put in aphabetical order. Then darken the circle for the correct answer.

**Sample**
Ⓐ hat
Ⓑ store
Ⓒ open
Ⓓ yesterday

**Time: 10 minutes**

**1.**
Ⓐ October
Ⓑ July
Ⓒ August
Ⓓ November

**2.**
Ⓐ sorry
Ⓑ silk
Ⓒ sand
Ⓓ such

**3.**
Ⓐ Garza, Evelyn
Ⓑ Adams, Derek
Ⓒ Gold, Albie
Ⓓ Costello, Irene

**4.**
Ⓐ climb
Ⓑ able
Ⓒ butter
Ⓓ almost

**5.**
Ⓐ clean
Ⓑ class
Ⓒ clown
Ⓓ clear

**6.**
Ⓐ Sunday
Ⓑ Thursday
Ⓒ Tuesday
Ⓓ Friday

**7.**
Ⓐ under
Ⓑ ugly
Ⓒ van
Ⓓ very

**8.** Which of these words would you find on a dictionary page with the guide words *globe* and *gobble*?
Ⓐ gold
Ⓑ goods
Ⓒ glow
Ⓓ gone

**GO ON** ⇨

# Test 9: Study Skills (Form A), page 2

**Directions:** For questions 9–12 look at this index from a book. Then darken the circle for the correct answer.

**Index**

Actors  62
Animals  40–45
Bicycles  73–80
   History of  75
Birds  91
Cars  83–90
Dangers  116
Earth  70
Electricity  119
   Uses of  123
Farms  5–15
Food  16

9. On which page will you read about actors?
   Ⓐ 62
   Ⓑ 70
   Ⓒ 40
   Ⓓ 73

10. What is the subheading for bicycles?
    Ⓐ How to ride a bicycle
    Ⓑ Different kinds of bicycles
    Ⓒ Racing bicycles
    Ⓓ History of bicycles

11. On which page will you learn about uses of electricity?
    Ⓐ 123
    Ⓑ 119
    Ⓒ 128
    Ⓓ 120

12. How many pages have information about food?
    Ⓐ 10 pages
    Ⓑ 1 page
    Ⓒ 3 pages
    Ⓓ 4 pages

13. Which section of the library would have a book about the Grand Canyon?
    Ⓐ biography
    Ⓑ history
    Ⓒ travel
    Ⓓ children

14. Which of these books would show the cities and towns in Texas?
    Ⓐ a story book
    Ⓑ an atlas
    Ⓒ a dictionary
    Ⓓ a health book

**STOP**

# Test 9: Study Skills (Form B)

**Directions:** For questions 1–11 darken the circle for the correct answer.

Use this table of contents to answer questions 1–3.

### Contents
**Unit I: Narrative Text**

**Time: 10 minutes**

1. What is this unit about?
   Ⓐ answering questions
   Ⓑ writing questions
   Ⓒ narrative text
   Ⓓ strategies

2. According to the table of contents, how many kinds of narrative questions are there?
   Ⓐ 14
   Ⓑ 5
   Ⓒ 8
   Ⓓ 6

3. On which pages will you learn how to write your own questions?
   Ⓐ 8–13
   Ⓑ 6–8
   Ⓒ 14–29
   Ⓓ 7–8

**Directions:** For questions 4–5 choose the word or name that would come *last* if the words were listed in alphabetical order.

4.
   Ⓐ cheese
   Ⓑ chatter
   Ⓒ church
   Ⓓ chickens

5.
   Ⓐ Stills, Rosie
   Ⓑ Soames, Karen
   Ⓒ Spencer, Kelvin
   Ⓓ Sanchez, Tomaso

# Test 9: Study Skills (Form B), page 2

**Directions:** For questions 6–8 study this map. Then darken the circle for the correct answer. Darken the circle for *Not given* if the information is *not* on the map.

KEY
Park
Mei's House
School

Fir
Oak
Daisy
Rose
Pine
Maple

**6.** On which street is the school?
Ⓐ Fir
Ⓑ Oak
Ⓒ Maple
Ⓓ Not given

**7.** If you want to go to the park, which street will you go to?
Ⓐ Fir
Ⓑ Rose
Ⓒ Pine
Ⓓ Not given

**8.** On what street is Mei's house?
Ⓐ Oak
Ⓑ Daisy
Ⓒ Maple
Ⓓ Not given

**Directions:** For questions 9–11 use the information below.

## THE LANDING OF THE PILGRIMS
Written and Illustrated by
JAMES DAUGHERTY

Landmark Books
Random House • New York

**9.** What is this kind of book page called?
Ⓐ table of contents
Ⓑ glossary
Ⓒ title page
Ⓓ index

**10.** Who did the art for this book?
Ⓐ Random House
Ⓑ Pilgrims
Ⓒ Landmark
Ⓓ James Daugherty

**11.** Who is the publisher of this book?
Ⓐ New York
Ⓑ James Daugherty
Ⓒ Random House
Ⓓ The Landing

# Test 9: Study Skills (Form C)

**Directions:** For questions 1–13 darken the circle for the correct answer.

Use this garden map to answer questions 1–4.

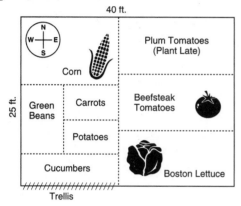

**Time: 10 minutes**

1. What is planted in the northwest corner of the garden?
   - Ⓐ Boston lettuce
   - Ⓑ corn
   - Ⓒ green beans
   - Ⓓ cucumbers

2. What should be planted late?
   - Ⓐ carrots
   - Ⓑ potatoes
   - Ⓒ beefsteak tomatoes
   - Ⓓ plum tomatoes

3. Which vegetable will grow along the trellis?
   - Ⓐ lettuce
   - Ⓑ cucumbers
   - Ⓒ corn
   - Ⓓ carrots

4. Which vegetable bed is not 20 feet wide?
   - Ⓐ corn
   - Ⓑ cucumbers
   - Ⓒ plum tomatoes
   - Ⓓ green beans

5. Which word would you find on a dictionary page that has the guide words *check* and *chew*?
   - Ⓐ cheap
   - Ⓑ chase
   - Ⓒ chief
   - Ⓓ chest

6. For which of these should you use an encyclopedia?
   - Ⓐ to find a news article about Rhode Island
   - Ⓑ to find the best way to get to Rhode Island by car
   - Ⓒ to learn about the history of Rhode Island
   - Ⓓ to read a story about children in Rhode Island

**GO ON ⇨**

# Test 9: Study Skills (Form C), page 2

**Directions:** Use the map to answer questions 7–11.

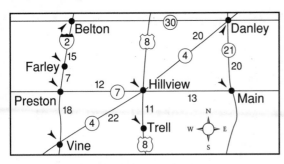

**7.** Which two highways pass through Hillview?
  (A) Highway 8 and Highway 4
  (B) Highway 21 and Highway 8
  (C) Highway 2 and Highway 4
  (D) Highway 21 and Highway 4

**8.** Which city is north of Vine?
  (A) Danley
  (B) Trell
  (C) Belton
  (D) Hillview

**9.** How many cities does Highway 4 pass through?
  (A) one
  (B) two
  (C) three
  (D) four

**10.** Which city is farthest south?
  (A) Farley
  (B) Vine
  (C) Trell
  (D) Main

**11.** How many miles is it from Preston to Hillview?
  (A) 12
  (B) 22
  (C) 13
  (D) 11

**12.** Which volume of the encyclopedia would you use to find information about the country of Turkey?

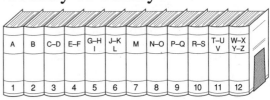

  (A) Volume 6
  (B) Volume 9
  (C) Volume 11
  (D) Volume 12

**13.** Where would you look to find out what the weather will be in a big city you are going to?
  (A) a magazine
  (B) a newspaper
  (C) a phone book
  (D) a dictionary

# Test 9: Study Skills (Form D)

**Directions:** For questions 1–16 darken the circle for the correct answer.

Use the table of contents below to answer questions 1–5.

---

**UNIT 5   Working with Adventure**

**Skills Lesson**

**Time: 10 minutes**

1. Who is the author of the story about forest rangers?
   A Mary Elting
   B Charles Coombs
   C David Lavine
   D Wayne Hyde

2. What will the skills lesson be about?
   A seeing organization
   B the Peace Corps
   C topical organization
   D helicopters

3. Who was David Lavine's co-author?
   A Ira Mandelbaum
   B Mary Elting
   C Wayne Hyde
   D Charles Coombs

4. How many pages long is the story about nurses on horseback?
   A 7
   B 8
   C 6
   D 9

5. What is Charles Coombs' story about?
   A bush flying
   B nursing
   C horseback riding
   D forest rangers

**GO ON ⇨**

# Test 9: Study Skills (Form D), page 2

**Directions:** Use the map to answer questions 6–11.

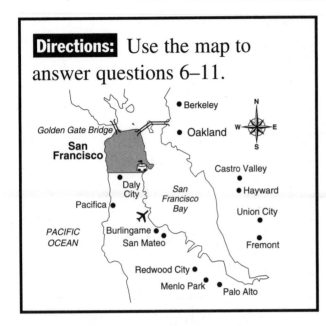

6. Which is the most northern city?
   Ⓐ Menlo Park
   Ⓑ Daly City
   Ⓒ Oakland
   Ⓓ Berkeley

7. Which is the most southern city?
   Ⓐ Redwood City
   Ⓑ Palo Alto
   Ⓒ Burlingame
   Ⓓ San Mateo

8. Which city is on the coast of the Pacific Ocean?
   Ⓐ Daly City
   Ⓑ Oakland
   Ⓒ Fremont
   Ⓓ Pacifica

9. Which city is west of San Francisco Bay?
   Ⓐ Hayward
   Ⓑ Daly City
   Ⓒ Union City
   Ⓓ Oakland

10. Which city is closest to the airport?
    Ⓐ Burlingame
    Ⓑ San Mateo
    Ⓒ Redwood City
    Ⓓ Castro Valley

11. Which city is east of San Francisco?
    Ⓐ Menlo Park
    Ⓑ Daly City
    Ⓒ Pacifica
    Ⓓ Oakland

12. Which section of the library has stories that were made up by the writers?
    Ⓐ gardening
    Ⓑ fiction
    Ⓒ cooking
    Ⓓ travel

# Test Practice Grade Three Answer Sheet

**STUDENT'S NAME**

**LAST** | **FIRST** | **MI**

(Name grid columns with bubbles A–Z)

**SCHOOL:**
**TEACHER:**
**FEMALE** ○   **MALE** ○

**BIRTH DATE**

| MONTH | DAY | YEAR |
|---|---|---|
| Jan ○ | ⓪ ⓪ | ⓪ ⓪ |
| Feb ○ | ① ① | ① ① |
| Mar ○ | ② ② | ② ② |
| Apr ○ | ③ ③ | ③ ③ |
| May ○ | ④ | ④ ④ |
| Jun ○ | ⑤ | ⑤ ⑤ |
| Jul ○ | ⑥ | ⑥ ⑥ |
| Aug ○ | ⑦ | ⑦ ⑦ |
| Sep ○ | ⑧ | ⑧ ⑧ |
| Oct ○ | ⑨ | ⑨ ⑨ |
| Nov ○ | | |
| Dec ○ | | |

**GRADE**   2   3   4   5   6

**TEST PRACTICE GRADE 3**
© Steck-Vaughn Company

---

## Test 1: Word Analysis (Form) ○A ○B ○C ○D

SA Ⓐ Ⓑ Ⓒ Ⓓ    1. Ⓐ Ⓑ Ⓒ Ⓓ    6. Ⓐ Ⓑ Ⓒ Ⓓ    11. Ⓐ Ⓑ Ⓒ Ⓓ    16. Ⓐ Ⓑ Ⓒ Ⓓ
SB Ⓐ Ⓑ Ⓒ Ⓓ    2. Ⓐ Ⓑ Ⓒ Ⓓ    7. Ⓐ Ⓑ Ⓒ Ⓓ    12. Ⓐ Ⓑ Ⓒ Ⓓ    17. Ⓐ Ⓑ Ⓒ Ⓓ
SC Ⓐ Ⓑ Ⓒ Ⓓ    3. Ⓐ Ⓑ Ⓒ Ⓓ    8. Ⓐ Ⓑ Ⓒ Ⓓ    13. Ⓐ Ⓑ Ⓒ Ⓓ    18. Ⓐ Ⓑ Ⓒ Ⓓ
SD Ⓐ Ⓑ Ⓒ Ⓓ    4. Ⓐ Ⓑ Ⓒ Ⓓ    9. Ⓐ Ⓑ Ⓒ Ⓓ    14. Ⓐ Ⓑ Ⓒ Ⓓ    19. Ⓐ Ⓑ Ⓒ Ⓓ
                5. Ⓐ Ⓑ Ⓒ Ⓓ   10. Ⓐ Ⓑ Ⓒ Ⓓ    15. Ⓐ Ⓑ Ⓒ Ⓓ    20. Ⓐ Ⓑ Ⓒ Ⓓ

## Test 2: Vocabulary (Form) ○A ○B ○C ○D

SA Ⓐ Ⓑ Ⓒ Ⓓ    4. Ⓐ Ⓑ Ⓒ Ⓓ    11. Ⓐ Ⓑ Ⓒ Ⓓ    18. Ⓐ Ⓑ Ⓒ Ⓓ    25. Ⓐ Ⓑ Ⓒ Ⓓ
SB Ⓐ Ⓑ Ⓒ Ⓓ    5. Ⓐ Ⓑ Ⓒ Ⓓ    12. Ⓐ Ⓑ Ⓒ Ⓓ    19. Ⓐ Ⓑ Ⓒ Ⓓ    26. Ⓐ Ⓑ Ⓒ Ⓓ
SC Ⓐ Ⓑ Ⓒ Ⓓ    6. Ⓐ Ⓑ Ⓒ Ⓓ    13. Ⓐ Ⓑ Ⓒ Ⓓ    20. Ⓐ Ⓑ Ⓒ Ⓓ    27. Ⓐ Ⓑ Ⓒ Ⓓ
SD Ⓐ Ⓑ Ⓒ Ⓓ    7. Ⓐ Ⓑ Ⓒ Ⓓ    14. Ⓐ Ⓑ Ⓒ Ⓓ    21. Ⓐ Ⓑ Ⓒ Ⓓ    28. Ⓐ Ⓑ Ⓒ Ⓓ
1. Ⓐ Ⓑ Ⓒ Ⓓ    8. Ⓐ Ⓑ Ⓒ Ⓓ    15. Ⓐ Ⓑ Ⓒ Ⓓ    22. Ⓐ Ⓑ Ⓒ Ⓓ
2. Ⓐ Ⓑ Ⓒ Ⓓ    9. Ⓐ Ⓑ Ⓒ Ⓓ    16. Ⓐ Ⓑ Ⓒ Ⓓ    23. Ⓐ Ⓑ Ⓒ Ⓓ
3. Ⓐ Ⓑ Ⓒ Ⓓ   10. Ⓐ Ⓑ Ⓒ Ⓓ    17. Ⓐ Ⓑ Ⓒ Ⓓ    24. Ⓐ Ⓑ Ⓒ Ⓓ

## Test 3: Reading Comprehension (Form) ○A ○B ○C ○D

SA Ⓐ Ⓑ Ⓒ Ⓓ    4. Ⓐ Ⓑ Ⓒ Ⓓ    9. Ⓐ Ⓑ Ⓒ Ⓓ    14. Ⓐ Ⓑ Ⓒ Ⓓ    19. Ⓐ Ⓑ Ⓒ Ⓓ
SB Ⓐ Ⓑ Ⓒ Ⓓ    5. Ⓐ Ⓑ Ⓒ Ⓓ   10. Ⓐ Ⓑ Ⓒ Ⓓ    15. Ⓐ Ⓑ Ⓒ Ⓓ    20. Ⓐ Ⓑ Ⓒ Ⓓ
1. Ⓐ Ⓑ Ⓒ Ⓓ    6. Ⓐ Ⓑ Ⓒ Ⓓ   11. Ⓐ Ⓑ Ⓒ Ⓓ    16. Ⓐ Ⓑ Ⓒ Ⓓ    21. Ⓐ Ⓑ Ⓒ Ⓓ
2. Ⓐ Ⓑ Ⓒ Ⓓ    7. Ⓐ Ⓑ Ⓒ Ⓓ   12. Ⓐ Ⓑ Ⓒ Ⓓ    17. Ⓐ Ⓑ Ⓒ Ⓓ    22. Ⓐ Ⓑ Ⓒ Ⓓ
3. Ⓐ Ⓑ Ⓒ Ⓓ    8. Ⓐ Ⓑ Ⓒ Ⓓ   13. Ⓐ Ⓑ Ⓒ Ⓓ    18. Ⓐ Ⓑ Ⓒ Ⓓ    23. Ⓐ Ⓑ Ⓒ Ⓓ

## Test 4: Spelling (Form) ○A ○B ○C ○D

S  Ⓐ Ⓑ Ⓒ Ⓓ    2. Ⓐ Ⓑ Ⓒ Ⓓ    4. Ⓐ Ⓑ Ⓒ Ⓓ    6. Ⓐ Ⓑ Ⓒ Ⓓ    8. Ⓐ Ⓑ Ⓒ Ⓓ
1. Ⓐ Ⓑ Ⓒ Ⓓ    3. Ⓐ Ⓑ Ⓒ Ⓓ    5. Ⓐ Ⓑ Ⓒ Ⓓ    7. Ⓐ Ⓑ Ⓒ Ⓓ    9. Ⓐ Ⓑ Ⓒ Ⓓ

# Test Practice Grade Three Answer Sheet

**Test 5: Language Mechanics (Form)** ○A ○B ○C ○D

| | | | | | | |
|---|---|---|---|---|---|---|
| SA Ⓐ Ⓑ Ⓒ Ⓓ | 1. Ⓐ Ⓑ Ⓒ Ⓓ | 5. Ⓐ Ⓑ Ⓒ Ⓓ | 9. Ⓐ Ⓑ Ⓒ Ⓓ | 13. Ⓐ Ⓑ Ⓒ Ⓓ |
| SB Ⓐ Ⓑ Ⓒ Ⓓ | 2. Ⓐ Ⓑ Ⓒ Ⓓ | 6. Ⓐ Ⓑ Ⓒ Ⓓ | 10. Ⓐ Ⓑ Ⓒ Ⓓ | 14. Ⓐ Ⓑ Ⓒ Ⓓ |
| SC Ⓐ Ⓑ Ⓒ Ⓓ | 3. Ⓐ Ⓑ Ⓒ Ⓓ | 7. Ⓐ Ⓑ Ⓒ Ⓓ | 11. Ⓐ Ⓑ Ⓒ Ⓓ | |
| | 4. Ⓐ Ⓑ Ⓒ Ⓓ | 8. Ⓐ Ⓑ Ⓒ Ⓓ | 12. Ⓐ Ⓑ Ⓒ Ⓓ | |

**Test 6: Language Expression (Form)** ○A ○B ○C ○D

| | | | | | |
|---|---|---|---|---|---|
| SA Ⓐ Ⓑ Ⓒ Ⓓ | 1. Ⓐ Ⓑ Ⓒ Ⓓ | 8. Ⓐ Ⓑ Ⓒ Ⓓ | 15. Ⓐ Ⓑ Ⓒ Ⓓ | 22. Ⓐ Ⓑ Ⓒ Ⓓ |
| SB Ⓐ Ⓑ Ⓒ Ⓓ | 2. Ⓐ Ⓑ Ⓒ Ⓓ | 9. Ⓐ Ⓑ Ⓒ Ⓓ | 16. Ⓐ Ⓑ Ⓒ Ⓓ | 23. Ⓐ Ⓑ Ⓒ Ⓓ |
| SC Ⓐ Ⓑ Ⓒ Ⓓ | 3. Ⓐ Ⓑ Ⓒ Ⓓ | 10. Ⓐ Ⓑ Ⓒ Ⓓ | 17. Ⓐ Ⓑ Ⓒ Ⓓ | 24. Ⓐ Ⓑ Ⓒ Ⓓ |
| SD Ⓐ Ⓑ Ⓒ Ⓓ | 4. Ⓐ Ⓑ Ⓒ Ⓓ | 11. Ⓐ Ⓑ Ⓒ Ⓓ | 18. Ⓐ Ⓑ Ⓒ Ⓓ | 25. Ⓐ Ⓑ Ⓒ Ⓓ |
| SE Ⓐ Ⓑ Ⓒ Ⓓ | 5. Ⓐ Ⓑ Ⓒ Ⓓ | 12. Ⓐ Ⓑ Ⓒ Ⓓ | 19. Ⓐ Ⓑ Ⓒ Ⓓ | 26. Ⓐ Ⓑ Ⓒ Ⓓ |
| | 6. Ⓐ Ⓑ Ⓒ Ⓓ | 13. Ⓐ Ⓑ Ⓒ Ⓓ | 20. Ⓐ Ⓑ Ⓒ Ⓓ | |
| | 7. Ⓐ Ⓑ Ⓒ Ⓓ | 14. Ⓐ Ⓑ Ⓒ Ⓓ | 21. Ⓐ Ⓑ Ⓒ Ⓓ | |

**Test 7: Mathematics Computation (Form)** ○A ○B ○C ○D

| | | | | | |
|---|---|---|---|---|---|
| SA Ⓐ Ⓑ Ⓒ Ⓓ | 1. Ⓐ Ⓑ Ⓒ Ⓓ | 5. Ⓐ Ⓑ Ⓒ Ⓓ | 9. Ⓐ Ⓑ Ⓒ Ⓓ | 13. Ⓐ Ⓑ Ⓒ Ⓓ |
| SB Ⓐ Ⓑ Ⓒ Ⓓ | 2. Ⓐ Ⓑ Ⓒ Ⓓ | 6. Ⓐ Ⓑ Ⓒ Ⓓ | 10. Ⓐ Ⓑ Ⓒ Ⓓ | 14. Ⓐ Ⓑ Ⓒ Ⓓ |
| | 3. Ⓐ Ⓑ Ⓒ Ⓓ | 7. Ⓐ Ⓑ Ⓒ Ⓓ | 11. Ⓐ Ⓑ Ⓒ Ⓓ | 15. Ⓐ Ⓑ Ⓒ Ⓓ |
| | 4. Ⓐ Ⓑ Ⓒ Ⓓ | 8. Ⓐ Ⓑ Ⓒ Ⓓ | 12. Ⓐ Ⓑ Ⓒ Ⓓ | |

**Test 8: Mathematics Concepts/Applications (Form)** ○A ○B ○C ○D

| | | | | | |
|---|---|---|---|---|---|
| SA Ⓐ Ⓑ Ⓒ Ⓓ | 1. Ⓐ Ⓑ Ⓒ Ⓓ | 6. Ⓐ Ⓑ Ⓒ Ⓓ | 11. Ⓐ Ⓑ Ⓒ Ⓓ | 16. Ⓐ Ⓑ Ⓒ Ⓓ |
| SB Ⓐ Ⓑ Ⓒ Ⓓ | 2. Ⓐ Ⓑ Ⓒ Ⓓ | 7. Ⓐ Ⓑ Ⓒ Ⓓ | 12. Ⓐ Ⓑ Ⓒ Ⓓ | 17. Ⓐ Ⓑ Ⓒ Ⓓ |
| | 3. Ⓐ Ⓑ Ⓒ Ⓓ | 8. Ⓐ Ⓑ Ⓒ Ⓓ | 13. Ⓐ Ⓑ Ⓒ Ⓓ | 18. Ⓐ Ⓑ Ⓒ Ⓓ |
| | 4. Ⓐ Ⓑ Ⓒ Ⓓ | 9. Ⓐ Ⓑ Ⓒ Ⓓ | 14. Ⓐ Ⓑ Ⓒ Ⓓ | 19. Ⓐ Ⓑ Ⓒ Ⓓ |
| | 5. Ⓐ Ⓑ Ⓒ Ⓓ | 10. Ⓐ Ⓑ Ⓒ Ⓓ | 15. Ⓐ Ⓑ Ⓒ Ⓓ | |

**Test 9: Study Skills (Form)** ○A ○B ○C ○D

| | | | | | |
|---|---|---|---|---|---|
| S Ⓐ Ⓑ Ⓒ Ⓓ | 1. Ⓐ Ⓑ Ⓒ Ⓓ | 5. Ⓐ Ⓑ Ⓒ Ⓓ | 9. Ⓐ Ⓑ Ⓒ Ⓓ | 13. Ⓐ Ⓑ Ⓒ Ⓓ |
| | 2. Ⓐ Ⓑ Ⓒ Ⓓ | 6. Ⓐ Ⓑ Ⓒ Ⓓ | 10. Ⓐ Ⓑ Ⓒ Ⓓ | 14. Ⓐ Ⓑ Ⓒ Ⓓ |
| | 3. Ⓐ Ⓑ Ⓒ Ⓓ | 7. Ⓐ Ⓑ Ⓒ Ⓓ | 11. Ⓐ Ⓑ Ⓒ Ⓓ | |
| | 4. Ⓐ Ⓑ Ⓒ Ⓓ | 8. Ⓐ Ⓑ Ⓒ Ⓓ | 12. Ⓐ Ⓑ Ⓒ Ⓓ | |